Directions: In the first exercise, write the letters of the alphabet, capital and small. In the second exercise, write the letter that comes after each letter you see.

Write the letters of the alphabet, capital and small.

Write the letter that comes after each letter you see.

m ___   q ___   n ___   p ___

g ___   t ___   r ___   x ___

u ___   c ___   s ___   d ___

f ___   w ___   h ___   y ___

k ___   o ___   i ___   a ___

1

Directions: In the first exercise, write the small letter for each capital letter. In the second exercise, fill in the missing letters. In the third exercise, write the letter that comes before the given letters.

Write the partner letters.

C ___   B ___   V ___   Y ___   F ___

A ___   H ___   W ___   Z ___   L ___

G ___   D ___   N ___   I ___   P ___

M ___   J ___   S ___   E ___   X ___

O ___   T ___   R ___   K ___   Q ___

U ___

Write the missing letters.

a ___ , ___   d ___   f   g ___

i   j ___   l ___   n   o ___   q

___   s   t ___   ___   w ___   y

___

Write the letter that comes before each letter you see.

___ f   ___ p   ___ y   ___ w   ___ o

___ n   ___ s   ___ c   ___ g   ___ v

___ j   ___ q   ___ z   ___ x   ___ l

Directions: In the first exercise, write the partner letter for each letter. In the second exercise, color the objects orange that contain a capital letter and its small letter.

Write the partner letter for each letter.

A _____	j _____	d _____	c _____	m _____
s _____	E _____	U _____	F _____	i _____
Z _____	R _____	h _____	V _____	l _____
K _____	B _____	G _____	o _____	n _____
t _____	Q _____	P _____	w _____	k _____

A _____	B _____	G _____	M _____	X _____
O _____	D _____	L _____	H _____	T _____
C _____	F _____	P _____	N _____	U _____
E _____	J _____	Q _____	S _____	V _____
Y _____	R _____	I _____	K _____	W _____

Color the objects orange if they contain partner letters.

B d   R r   L t   Z z   E e   P q   Y y

H q   M n   N m   P p   U v   W y   H h

S s   F g   N n   O c   W v   X x   I i

Directions: In each row draw a ring around each word that contains the letter shown at the beginning of the row.

C c	catch	cookies	much	Carl	doll
F f	after	Fred	funny	gift	milk
H h	hello	moth	night	Halloween	here
A a	ball	please	Ann	Mary	fast
T t	something	just	Tom	rest	home
R r	better	poor	Ray	here	run
M m	came	not	Mark	must	some
N n	green	make	down	find	Nan
W w	away	cow	took	Willy	new
L l	Larry	all	there	look	help
O o	boat	sang	Oz	told	know
G g	looking	big	walk	good	Glenn
E e	everything	Ellen	sat	need	dime
B b	birthday	big	all	Bill	ball
D d	down	doll	Dan	find	boat
I i	into	Betty	live	I	went
K k	know	Ken	knew	duck	tell

4

Directions: Say the name of each picture. On the line below the picture, write the capital and small forms of the letter with which it begins.

5

Directions: Read each sentence, and draw a ring around any word in which you see and hear the beginning consonants **Q**, **S**, **V**, **W**, **Y**, or **Z**. Then choose two sentences, and draw a picture of each in the boxes below.

Draw a ring around each word that begins with **q**, **s**, **v**, **w**, **y**, or **z**.

1. The quilt on my bed is white and yellow.

2. A jet passed over our yard yesterday.

3. Vincent planted some pretty violets near the window.

4. The zipper on Steve's jacket was broken.

5. She went to the store for a quart of milk.

6. Would you like to wear your yellow skirt today?

7. We watched the queen as she sat on the throne.

8. Susan went to bed because she was sleepy.

9. Did you see the snake near the grape vines?

10. We saw six zebras at the zoo.

Draw pictures about any two of the sentences. Put the number of each sentence in the corner box.

Directions: Say the name of each picture. Write on the line the consonant you hear in the middle of each word.

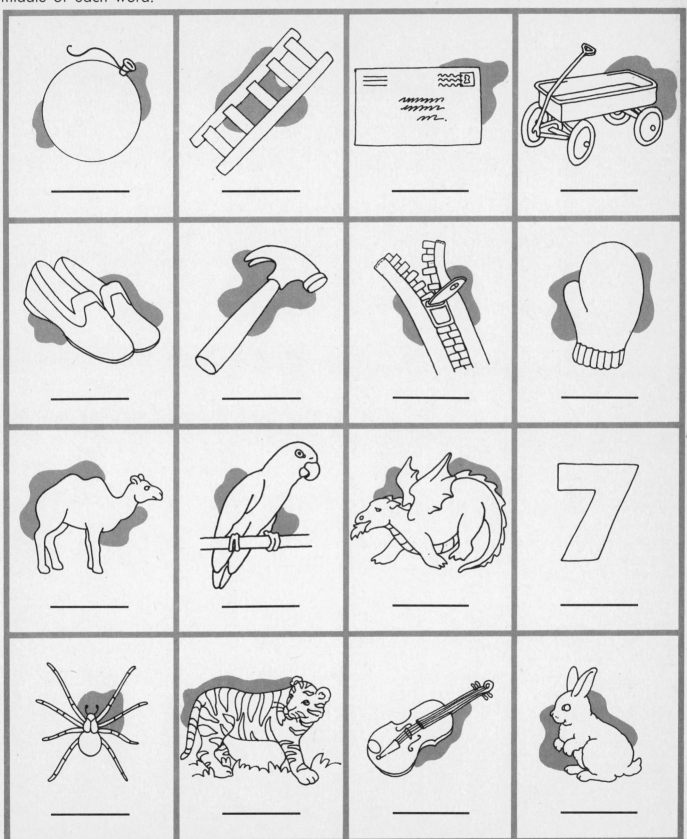

Directions: Say the name of each picture. Color all the pictures in each row whose names have the same ending consonant sound as the given letter.

t				
k				
p				
x				
l				

Directions: In the first exercise, write the consonant you hear at the beginning of the name of each picture. In the second exercise, write the consonant you hear at the end. In the third exercise, write the consonant you hear at the beginning and end.

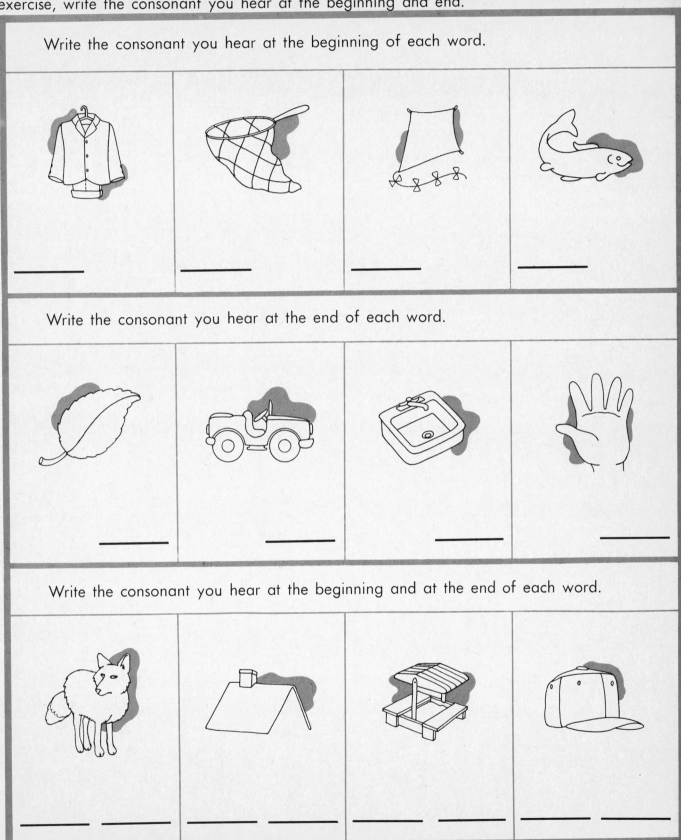

Write the consonant you hear at the beginning of each word.

Write the consonant you hear at the end of each word.

Write the consonant you hear at the beginning and at the end of each word.

Directions: Read the words listed below, and write them in the correct columns according to the positions of the given consonants.

vat	funny	pedal	music
wagon	cowboy	yellow	bike
hated	soap	room	hurry
near	cab	tow	dog
gas	happy	leaf	comic

	Beginning Consonant	Middle Consonant	Ending Consonant
p	_____	_____	_____
d	_____	_____	_____
b	_____	_____	_____
l	_____	_____	_____
m	_____	_____	_____
s	_____	_____	_____
r	_____	_____	_____
n	_____	_____	_____
t	_____	_____	_____
g	_____	_____	_____

Directions: Write the words that contain a hard **C** under the picture of the cake. Write the words that contain a soft **C** under the picture of the pencil.

> **REMEMBER:** When **c** is followed by **e**, **i**, or **y**, the **c** is usually soft. Soft **c** stands for the sound **s** stands for.

grocery	doctor	candy	recess	cement
decide	cookies	price	cattle	corn
force	decorate	crib	cow	grace
actor	cellar	palace	carriage	cemetery

cake

1. _____
2. _____
3. _____
4. _____
5. _____
6. _____
7. _____
8. _____
9. _____
10. _____

pencil

1. _____
2. _____
3. _____
4. _____
5. _____
6. _____
7. _____
8. _____
9. _____
10. _____

Directions: In each box draw a line connecting the words that have the same sound of **G**. Then write the hard-**G** words and the soft-**G** words on the correct lines below.

REMEMBER: When **g** is followed by **e**, **i**, or **y**, the **g** is usually soft. Soft **g** stands for the sound **j** stands for.

Draw a line connecting the words in each box having the same sound of **g**.

page	game	ugly	large	orange	huge
flag	engine	gold	giraffe	sugar	organ
golden	agree	gum	giant	savage	grace
pigeon	arrange	ginger	gay	garden	plunge

Write the hard-**g** words and the soft-**g** words.

Hard **g** _____   Soft **g** _____

_____   _____

_____   _____

_____   _____

_____   _____

_____   _____

_____   _____

_____   _____

_____   _____

_____   _____

Directions: In the first exercise, draw a ring around each word having soft **C** or soft **G**. In the second exercise, draw a ring around each word having hard **C** or hard **G**.

REMEMBER: When **c** or **g** is followed by **e**, **i**, or **y**, **c** or **g** usually has a soft sound.

Draw a ring around each word having soft **c** or soft **g**.

ice	can	lace	came	fancy	gym
grass	giant	rice	large	huge	wig
cage	center	celery	because	clean	bicycle
hug	city	judge	Cindy	face	cookies
game	engine	dance	leg	ceiling	police
fence	garden	price	guess	magic	place
tag	nice	bridge	giraffe	gem	cover
Virginia	again	cement	agent	crime	gadget
grant	certain	Gerald	gentleman	gypsy	actor
ginger	orange	doctor	gate	page	Grace

Draw a ring around each word having hard **c** or hard **g**.

1. Janice gave me a cone for the ice cream.

2. Come and look at the copper kettle.

3. Apricots and carrots are good for children.

4. Joe gave him a gallon jug to keep the juice cold.

5. Green is a nice color for a coat.

6. Lance gave the children in my class ginger cookies.

7. The car gained speed as it raced past the corner.

8. The actor came on the stage once again.

Directions: From the list of words choose a word to complete each sentence. Read each sentence carefully. Find the words that contain the hard and soft sounds of **C** and **G**, and write them on the correct lines below.

1. Yesterday I skated on the _____.   doctor

2. The _____ will leave the pills.   gave

3. There is a large garden around the queen's _____.   ice

4. Clare will plant the flowers near the _____.   giant

5. Connie _____ Gerald a bigger slice of bread.   gate

6. Alice paid a dime for the _____.   palace

7. The _____ is the tallest animal in the zoo.   candy

8. The _____ in the story was ten feet tall.   giraffe

Hard **c** _____   Soft **c** _____

_____   _____

_____   _____

_____   _____

Hard **g** _____   Soft **g** _____

_____   _____

_____   _____

14

Directions: In the first section, write the name of the picture, and draw a ring around the vowel. In the second section, say the names of the pictures, and color the ones in which you hear the short vowel **A**.

Write the name of each picture, and draw a ring around the vowel.

_____   _____   _____   _____   _____

Say the name of each picture, and color those in which you hear the short vowel **A**.

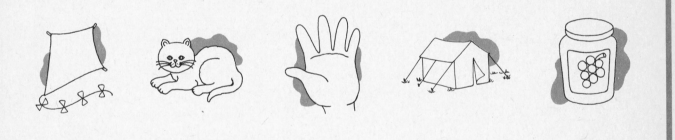

15

Directions: Read each sentence. Find the short-**A** words, and write them on the lines at the right. Then draw a picture of what the sentence tells about.

The big man has a black hat.

Pat swam to save Jack.

Dad came home in a cab.

The fan blew Ann's hat off.

The deer ran faster than the rabbit.

1. _____
2. _____
3. _____
4. _____
5. _____
6. _____
7. _____
8. _____
9. _____
10. _____
11. _____
12. _____
13. _____
14. _____
15. _____
16. _____

Directions: In the first section, write the name of each picture, and draw a ring around the vowel. In the second section, find a word in column 2 that rhymes with a word in column 1. Write the rhyming word on the line.

Write the name of each picture, and draw a ring around the vowel.

Read each word in column 1. Find a word in column 2 that rhymes with it and write the rhyming word on the line.

1	2	1	2	1	2
kick _____	fig	hip _____	tin	wig _____	hit
rip _____	hill	pin _____	big	lit _____	rig
dig _____	sick	pig _____	lip	dip _____	bin
bill _____	lip	did _____	lid	tin _____	tip

17

Directions: Find the short-**A** words and the short-**I** words in the list, and write them on the correct lines.

REMEMBER: If a word or syllable has only one vowel and it comes at the beginning or between two consonants, that vowel usually stands for a short sound.

lamp	late	Jim	gift	if	back	am
it	cake	cat	ham	died	Zip	time
hit	map	rain	an	sip	tick	Ann
ask	dime	fish	milk	ran	at	tip
pin	dish	wax	will	rap	hike	Sam

Short **A**

Short **I**

_____ _____   _____ _____

_____ _____   _____ _____

_____ _____   _____ _____

_____ _____   _____ _____

_____ _____   _____ _____

_____ _____   _____ _____

Directions: In the first section, write the name of the picture, and draw a ring around the vowel. In the second section, complete each sentence, using all the words at the right.

_____	_____	_____	_____
_____	_____	_____	_____

Complete each sentence, using all the words at the right.

1. Quack is _____.	a fat duck
2. The big jug is _____.	full milk of
3. Can Bud _____?	ham the cut
4. The tub is _____.	suds of full
5. Gus will run and jump _____.	the camp at

Directions: Write a short sentence about each picture.

1.	2.	3.	4.	5.

1. _____

   _____

2. _____

   _____

3. _____

   _____

4. _____

   _____

5. _____

   _____

Directions: Read the words in the first column. Make new words by changing the short **U** to short **A** and then to short **I**. Write the new words on the correct lines.

Make two new words by changing the vowel.

	Short **A**	Short **I**
fun	_____	_____
us	_____	_____
bug	_____	_____
hum	_____	_____
hut	_____	_____
but	_____	_____
luck	_____	_____
tuck	_____	_____
sunk	_____	_____
puck	_____	_____
bud	_____	_____
rug	_____	_____
must	_____	_____
stuck	_____	_____
truck	_____	_____

21

Directions: Draw a ring around the name of each picture.

fox box ox bat	cot cut cat cod	gap pig pup pop
us as ox ax	pat pit pot top	log dog lag lug
mud pan map mop	box fox fix six	tap top pot pat
dig dug log dog	rug rag rod rid	lock lack lick luck
sack sock sick suck	dot hill doll dill	rods dots rack rock

Directions: At the top, write the name of each picture, and draw a ring around the vowel. Read the story and underline each word containing short **O**. Write those words on the lines.

Write the name of each picture, and draw a ring around the vowel.

_____	_____	_____	_____

Draw a line under each word containing short **O**, and write those words on the lines.

A Summer Picnic

Last summer the Todd family went on a picnic. They had a pot of beans, hot dogs, and pop. After lunch Dot played with her doll, and Mom found rocks to put into the hobby box. Bobby, the baby, saw something green hopping near the pond and tried to catch it. He tripped over a log and fell into the water. His dad caught him and saved him. The green frog hopped away.

_____   _____   _____

_____   _____   _____

_____   _____   _____

_____   _____   _____

_____   _____   _____

_____   _____   _____

Directions: Find the short **I** and the short **O** words in the list, and print them in the correct spaces.

lit	Timmy	him	white	pocket	slip
chip	Bobby	lock	fox	Sally	fit
those	kite	sail	sat	hot	frog
stoop	fiddle	rope	rock	cute	fast
chop	Tom	thin	with	note	but

Short **O**

Short **I**

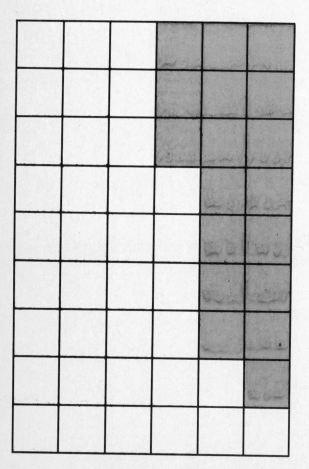

Directions: In the first section, make two new words by changing the vowel in each given word. In the second section, complete the sentences using the new words.

Make two new words by changing the vowel.

cat _____ _____   lamp _____ _____

tip _____ _____   cob _____ _____

on _____ _____   dig _____ _____

Use the new words from the list above to complete the sentences.

1. The baby is sleeping on the _____.

2. When I get home I will _____ the cake.

3. I like to watch my _____ spin.

4. She heard a small _____ on the door.

5. When the dog hurt his leg he began to _____.

6. When John fell he got a _____ on his head.

7. Dad paid the man when he rode in the _____.

8. A baby bear is called a _____.

9. Mary was eating _____ apple.

10. Mom was _____ a hurry to go to the game.

11. The little puppy _____ a big hole.

12. I love my brown _____.

Directions: Say the name of each picture. Write the word under the picture, and draw a ring around the vowel.

Directions: In the first section, write the name of each picture on the line below it. In the second section, draw a ring around the name of each picture.

Write the name of each picture.

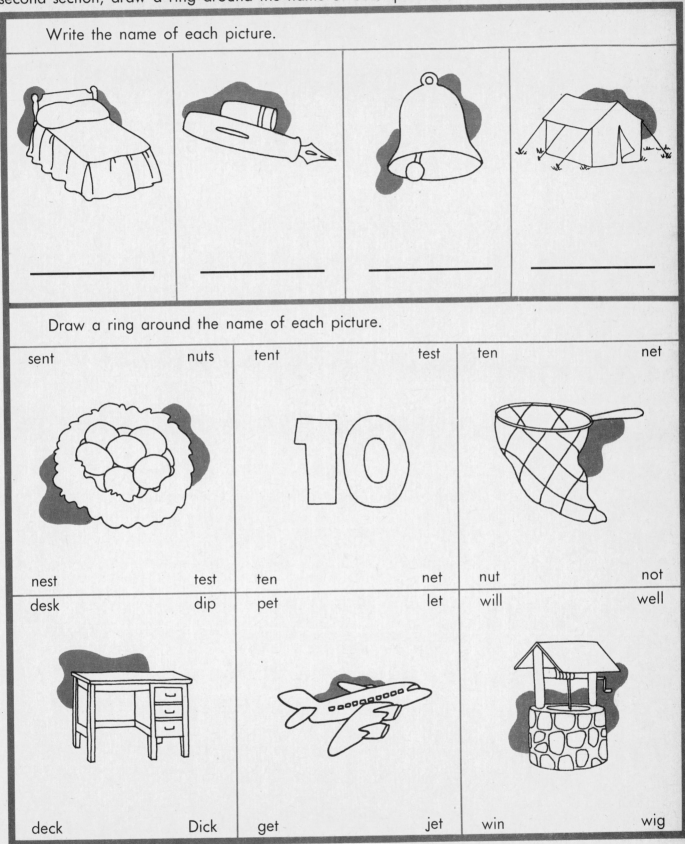

Draw a ring around the name of each picture.

sent nuts	tent test	ten net
nest test	ten net	nut not
desk dip	pet let	will well
deck Dick	get jet	win wig

Directions: In the first section, complete each sentence by choosing a word from the list. In the second section, write two rhyming words for each given word.

Complete the sentences.

bed	beg	well	Tell	leg
wet	ten	men	met	fed

1. The mother bird _____ her babies.

2. It is very dark and _____ today.

3. How did you hurt your _____ ?

4. My dog can sit up and _____ for his supper.

5. _____ us what you and Mom saw downtown.

6. Jack has _____ sheets of paper to write on.

7. Make your _____ when you get up.

8. Dad went with two other _____ to the game.

9. Mom _____ me as I went in the door.

10. You did very _____ on the test.

Write two rhyming words. The given beginning letters will help you.

beg	pet	hen	bell	bed
l ____	g ____	m ____	f ____	r ____
p ____	w ____	p ____	s ____	l ____

Directions: Look at each picture, and write its name under it. Color all the pictures.

Directions: Make three new words out of each word at the left. For each word a new beginning consonant, a new ending consonant, and a new vowel are listed for you. Write the missing letters in the spaces to form each new word.

	New Beginning Consonants	New Ending Consonants	New Vowels
pen	h __ __	__ __ t	__ i __
not	g __ __	__ __ d	__ u __
pot	n __ __	__ __ d	__ i __
bat	f __ __	__ __ d	__ i __
pet	g __ __	__ __ g	__ o __
run	b __ __	__ __ g	__ a __
man	c __ __	__ __ p	__ e __
bad	h __ __	__ __ g	__ i __
ham	j __ __	__ __ d	__ i __
big	w __ __	__ __ t	__ e __
cup	p __ __	__ __ b	__ a __
sat	h __ __	__ __ d	__ i __
top	h __ __	__ __ t	__ a __
let	m __ __	__ __ d	__ o __
hum	g __ __	__ __ g	__ a __
jot	c __ __	__ __ b	__ e __

30

Directions: Find a word in column 2 that rhymes with a word in column 1, and write it on the line.

> **REMEMBER:** If a one-part word or syllable has two vowels, the first vowel usually stands for a long sound and the second is silent.
>
> If a word or syllable has one vowel and it comes at the end of the word or syllable, that vowel usually stands for a long sound.

Column 1		Column 2	Column 1		Column 2
bone	_____	date	fire	_____	here
tune	_____	time	rule	_____	hire
dime	_____	note	vase	_____	ride
late	_____	June	hide	_____	mule
see	_____	cone	fear	_____	cure
vote	_____	be	pure	_____	case
tape	_____	joke	wife	_____	gave
heel	_____	cape	seal	_____	fine
poke	_____	made	shine	_____	life
like	_____	deep	yeast	_____	goat
wade	_____	feel	coat	_____	deal
keep	_____	bike	save	_____	least

Directions: In the first section, choose the correct word to complete each sentence, and write it on the line. Read the story in the second section, and draw a ring around each word having a long-vowel sound in it.

Complete the sentences.

1. Three bikes plus two bikes are _____ bikes.   vase

2. You may put the flowers in this _____.   hole

3. It is wise to _____ your money.   five

4. At three o'clock you may go _____.   rake

5. Gather the leaves with a _____.   save

6. The puppy dug a _____ in the ground.   home

7. Put the ice _____ into the glass.   fire

8. We will _____ a birthday cake.   ride

9. Never, never play with _____.   bake

10. Every day I _____ to school on the bus.   cube

Draw a ring around each word having a long-vowel sound in it.

A Day in June

It was a fine day in the month of June. The sky was blue, and birds sang in the trees. The sun shone through the wind-tossed leaves and danced on the blades of grass.

Jane White gazed out her window at all this, but she was not happy. She had offered to stay home with Grandma while the rest of the family went to the lake. Now she had nothing to do.

Suddenly she remembered the book that Sue had lent her. As she and Grandma began to read the book, they began to dream of boats, deep seas, and lands that were far away. Jane was no longer sad. She was glad that she had stayed home with Grandma.

32 _____

Directions: In the first section, write the name of each picture on the line below it. In the second section, change each word to a long-vowel word.

Write the name of the picture.

_____	_____	_____	_____

_____	_____	_____	_____

Change the words to long-vowel words.

cap _____   ran _____   tap _____

tub _____   cub _____   hug _____

got _____   hop _____   fed _____

hid _____   red _____   kit _____

33

Directions: Draw a ring around each short-vowel word.

A	I	U	O	E
can	kite	cute	hop	eat
came	kit	bun	home	peg
had	rip	tub	hot	red
late	ride	muff	bone	desk
man	milk	cube	lost	peak
rain	pick	nuts	got	neck
fat	tin	flute	pop	feel
mail	time	fun	note	web
gas	lick	fuse	log	let
jam	wide	tune	tone	seem
tame	fin	tub	Tom	bed
lap	pipe	hum	dog	reap
an	pill	rule	rock	tent
cab	hid	cub	cone	peel
wax	fix	tube	goat	jet
name	pine	up	block	went
tail	miss	use	rode	she
Sam	hide	rub	road	Ben
ask	is	rust	lock	pelt
ate	big	pure	top	deep
last	dime	hut	job	pen
sand	lift	us	no	elf
pain	hill	bug	box	men
Ann	hike	Luke	toss	leap

Directions: Draw a ring around each short-vowel word.

34

Directions: Make two words out of each compound word. Write the new words on the lines.

railway _____ _____

sunshine _____ _____

playmate _____ _____

beehive _____ _____

beanbag _____ _____

pancake _____ _____

wayside _____ _____

airway _____ _____

hillside _____ _____

milkman _____ _____

milkweed _____ _____

smokehouse _____ _____

peanuts _____ _____

treetop _____ _____

sailboat _____ _____

driveway _____ _____

sidetrack _____ _____

Directions: Say the name of each picture. In the box beside each picture, write the number of syllables you hear in the name of the picture.

REMEMBER: If you hear one vowel sound in a word, the word has one syllable.

If you hear two vowel sounds in a word, the word has two syllables.

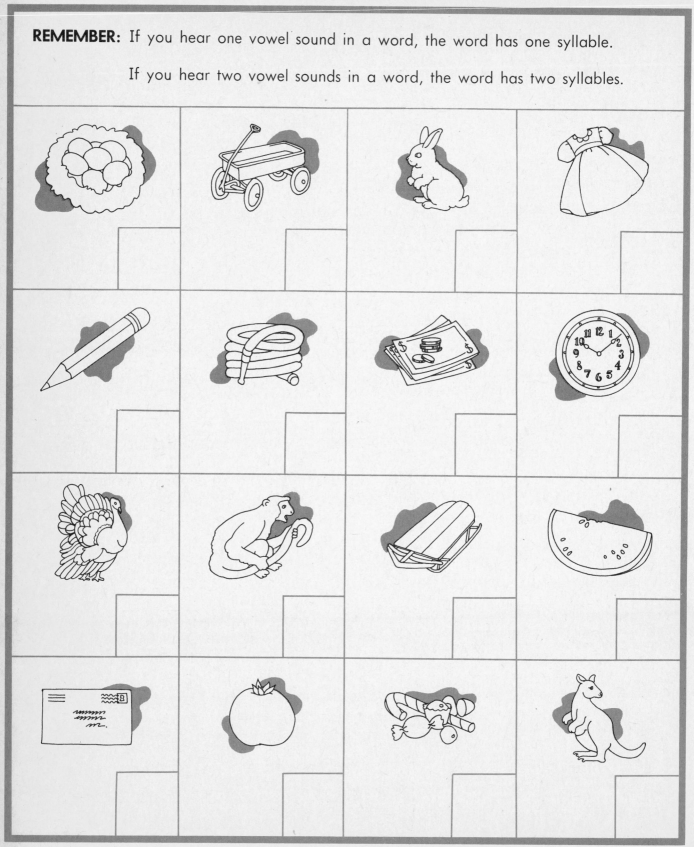

Directions: In the first exercise, write the name of each picture. In the second exercise, write the number of vowels seen in each word and the number of vowel sounds heard.

Write the name of each picture.

_____	_____	_____	_____
_____	_____	_____	_____

Write the number of vowels you see in each word, and then write the number of vowels you hear in each word.

	Vowels			**Vowels**	
	Seen	Heard		Seen	Heard
cabin	_____	_____	basement	_____	_____
hotel	_____	_____	wigwam	_____	_____
milk	_____	_____	noses	_____	_____
Peter	_____	_____	magic	_____	_____
jeep	_____	_____	kitten	_____	_____
safety	_____	_____	secret	_____	_____
race	_____	_____	easy	_____	_____
music	_____	_____	tiger	_____	_____
rabbit	_____	_____	lifted	_____	_____
supper	_____	_____	pony	_____	_____

Directions: Write the vowels that you can both see and hear in each word.

REMEMBER: If you hear two vowel sounds in a word, the word has two syllables.

	Vowels Seen	Vowel Sounds Heard		Vowels Seen	Vowel Sounds Heard
program	_____	_____	basket	_____	_____
basement	_____	_____	unbend	_____	_____
cactus	_____	_____	mitten	_____	_____
bacon	_____	_____	safety	_____	_____
pencil	_____	_____	visit	_____	_____
music	_____	_____	selfish	_____	_____
stocking	_____	_____	cannot	_____	_____
apron	_____	_____	cabin	_____	_____
until	_____	_____	hungry	_____	_____
puppy	_____	_____	yellow	_____	_____
picnic	_____	_____	secret	_____	_____
hopping	_____	_____	refill	_____	_____
happy	_____	_____	kitchen	_____	_____
travel	_____	_____	heated	_____	_____

Directions: At the top, write the words having one syllable in column 1; those with two syllables in column 2; those with three syllables in column 3. At the bottom, draw a ring around the numeral that tells how many syllables you hear in each word.

Write the words in the proper columns.

love	window	please	pickle	park
happiness	September	flatter	face	suddenly
forget	tiger	understand	spring	committee
grandfather	butterfly	explain	blanket	one
		soup		

One Syllable   **Two Syllables**   **Three Syllables**

_____ _____ _____

_____ _____ _____

_____ _____ _____

_____ _____ _____

_____ _____ _____

_____ _____ _____

Say the name of each picture. Then draw a ring around the numeral that tells how many syllables you hear.

| 1   2
 3   4 | 1   2
 3   4 | 1   2
 3   4 | 1   2
 3   4 |

39

Directions: In the first section, say the name of each picture, and write the blend that you hear. In the second section, complete each sentence by choosing the correct word or words from the list.

Write the blend you hear.

_____	_____	_____
_____	_____	_____

Use the words from the list to complete the sentences.

crowd	trip	brush	proud	green
drum	fruit	crowned	brooms	trunk

1. The bowl was filled with many kinds of _____.

2. The _____ watched as the queen was _____.

3. Joe is packing his _____ for the _____.

4. The cows were in the _____ pasture.

5. Brenda is _____ to play her new _____.

6. Put the _____ and the _____ in the closet.

LESSON 16: RECOGNIZING L BLENDS

Directions: In the first section, think of two more words beginning with the same blend as the given word. Then write the blends on the lines. In the second section, use an **L** blend to complete the unfinished word in each sentence.

Write two more words for each of the **L** blends. The given ending letters will help you.

black	_____ _____ ue	_____ _____ ock
clean	_____ _____ ock	_____ _____ ip
flat	_____ _____ ag	_____ _____ y
glad	_____ _____ ow	_____ _____ ue
plant	_____ _____ ay	_____ _____ ease
sled	_____ _____ eep	_____ _____ ide

Use an **L** blend to complete the unfinished word in each sentence.

1. The _____ock strikes every hour.

2. The wind stopped _____owing late last night.

3. The _____umbers worked on the water pipes today.

4. The class made a pretty new _____ag for the parade.

5. The plane _____ew over the high buildings.

6. The turtle was so _____ow that we named him Pokey.

7. Clare's plant has leaves that hang to the _____oor.

8. Jack's toy boat _____oated smoothly over the water.

41

Directions: Say the name of each picture, and draw a ring around the blend with which it begins. Color the pictures.

sp	spr	sm	sn	str	spl	sw	sm
str	sm	sw	sl	sk	squ	sn	sp

sm	sp	st	str	sp	squ	sw	sm
sc	sw	sn	sk	sl	st	sn	sp

sp	spl	sw	sm	sp	str	sl	sc
sk	st	str	sn	sw	sm	spl	sn

str	squ	sl	sp	sm	sw	scr	spr
sw	sm	st	sc	sp	str	sk	sw

42

Directions: In the first section, draw a ring around the correct word that completes each sentence. In the second section, write the correct **S** blend on the line beside each word.

Draw a ring around the correct word to complete each sentence.

1. The innkeeper decided to (sweep, rock) the magic rug.

2. He served him (windy, roast) duck on a big plate.

3. Quick as a wink Tom (scampered, swept) after the black dog.

4. Joan (signaled, sneezed) and awakened the baby.

5. Ann (spent, served) her free time helping poor children.

6. Dad (spoke, splashed) to David about the trip.

7. The (smoke, spell) came out of the barn door.

8. The beaver (splashed, soaked) around the pond.

9. The excited children (screamed, swept) with delight.

10. Most of the campers knew how to (sly, swim) in the lake.

11. Mom had to (sew, screw) the hooks into the wall.

12. The teacher asked Fred to (speak, string) a little louder.

Read the words in the list. Then read the list of **s** blends. Find the **s** blend that is used in each word and write it on the line.

skid	_____	sn	stamp	_____	str
smile	_____	sw	spray	_____	scr
scale	_____	sk	stream	_____	st
sniff	_____	sc	spell	_____	spr
sweep	_____	sm	scrub	_____	sp

43

Directions: In the first section, draw a ring around the blend in each word. In the second section, find the missing word, and write it on the line.

Draw a ring around each blend.

trot	plow	smile	snore
dried	clown	squeeze	score
flames	blend	straw	scamper
creek	clean	swing	string
slipper	sparkle	frame	place
driveway	gray	blowing	feast
class	floor	smart	dressed
slip	tramp	proud	exclaimed
most	graze	sleepy	spending

Read each sentence. Find the missing word, and write it on the line.

1. Glen helped Bruce _____ the green hedges.

skip
clip
slip

2. In winter we like to _____ on our sleds.

toast
roast
coast

3. The strong _____ spread the flames.

squeeze
breeze
freeze

4. Frank crossed the green _____ near the cabin.

grass
glass
class

5. Please pick up the _____ of paper on the floor.

traps
scraps
straps

6. Clare drove her truck into the _____.

bravely
grateful
driveway

Directions: Complete each sentence by choosing the correct word from the list.

street	scrub	creatures	struck	bricks
prince	glass	string	truck	Fred
cry	bread	brown	scream	introduce

1. Tie the packages with _____.

2. Yesterday I had a _____ of tomato juice.

3. Every Saturday I help my mom _____ the floor.

4. Living things are called _____.

5. The third little pig built a house with _____.

6. The son of a king is a _____.

7. The accident happened on our _____.

8. Dad bought a _____ tie to match his suit.

9. During the storm the lightning _____ our tree.

10. The little boy's first name is _____.

11. The opposite of ''laugh'' is _____.

12. The eagle flew overhead with a loud _____.

13. Will you _____ your aunt to me?

14. Please pass me a piece of _____.

15. The driver hopped into his _____ and drove away.

Directions: In the first section, add **Y** to each blend, and write the new word on the line. Say the words to yourself, and listen for the long sound of **Y**. In the second section, write answers to the questions, using complete sentences.

Add **y** to each blend. Write the new word on the line.

fr _____   cr _____

tr _____   dr _____

sk _____   sl _____

fl _____   spr _____

Use the words you have just made. Write your answers in complete sentences.

1. What is the insect that bothers us during the summer months?

_____

_____

2. What do babies sometimes do when they cannot have what they want?

_____

_____

3. If I want to make a fire what kind of wood must I use?

_____

_____

4. Where must we look in order to see clouds?

_____

_____

Directions: In the first section, write **LI** if **Y** has the sound of long **I**; write **LE** if **Y** has almost the sound of long **E**. In the second section, complete each sentence by using a word from the list.

REMEMBER: When **Y** comes at the end of a word, **Y** is a vowel.
When **Y** is the only vowel at the end of a one-part word, **Y** has the sound of long **I**.

When **Y** is the only vowel at the end of a word of more than one part, **Y** usually has almost the sound of long **E**.

In the list below, if **Y** has the sound of long **I**, write **LI**; if **Y** has almost the sound of long **E**, write **LE**.

every _____	sky _____	swiftly _____	bunny _____
silently _____	history _____	fly _____	why _____
try _____	grocery _____	family _____	cry _____

Complete each sentence, using a word from the list.

slippery	pretty	jelly
family	buggy	grocery

1. The grape _____ has a

   _____ purple color.

2. We pushed the baby to the _____ in

   her _____.

3. Fred fell as he skated on the _____ ice.

4. There are two children in our _____.

Directions: In the first section, write the name of each picture. The list of words will help you. In the second section, read each word, and write **C** if **Y** is used as a consonant; **LI** if **Y** has the sound of long **I**; and **LE** if **Y** has almost the sound of long **E**.

Write the name of each picture.

fairy	party	bunny	puppy	baby	muddy
pretty	carry	candy	twenty	Daddy	dolly

REMEMBER: When **Y** comes at the beginning of a word, **Y** is a consonant.

Write **C** if **Y** is used as a consonant; **LI** if **Y** has the sound of long **I**; and **LE** if **Y** has almost the sound of long **E**.

many _____	my _____	yes _____	every _____	cry _____
year _____	sky _____	fly _____	windy _____	you _____
by _____	yet _____	pretty _____	try _____	candy _____
yard _____	happy _____	yeast _____	lovely _____	dry _____
sweetly _____	yellow _____	why _____	your _____	sly _____

Directions: Read the story. Underline each word that has **Y** in it. Write the underlined words in the correct columns at the bottom of the page. Do not repeat a word.

Cooky, the Ice-Cream Man

One afternoon my brother Craig and I heard a jet go over our yard.

"Oh, isn't it a beauty?" I asked.

"Where is it?" I heard Craig cry.

"Over there, in the sky above the yellow house," I yelled. "Do you see it yet?"

"I would like to fly a jet like that one," said Craig.

"Let's try to save our money so that we can have our own plane when we grow up. Here's twenty cents to start," I said.

Just then, down the street came the jingling of a bell and the blowing of a whistle. We both knew that it was Cooky, the ice-cream man. His ice-cream bars were big and thick and creamy. Craig looked at me, and I looked at him. I knew what he had in mind. "Why not?" I said. "It is awfully hot and dry."

As we ate the ice cream, Craig said, "You know, we'd better start soon to save for the airplane, or we'll be fifty years old before we get it."

"Yes," I said. "We'd better start tomorrow."

Y as a consonant	**Y** as long **E**	**Y** as long **I**
_____	_____	_____
_____	_____	_____
_____	_____	_____
_____	_____	_____
_____	_____	_____
_____	_____	_____
_____		

Directions: In the first section, look at each picture, and draw a ring around the **AR**, **OR**, **IR**, **UR**, or **ER** in its name. In the second section, complete the words by writing **AR**, **OR**, **IR**, **UR**, or **ER** in each space.

Draw a ring around the **ar**, **or**, **ir**, **ur**, or **er** in the name of each picture.

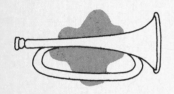

h o r n

s t a r

b i r d

t i g e r

c h u r c h

Complete each word by writing **ar**, **or**, **ir**, **ur**, or **er** in the space.

g_____l   c_____k   sk_____t   sc_____f

t_____key   j_____   h_____n   moth_____

c_____n   b_____d   pap_____   slipp_____

g_____den   st_____m   b_____n   p_____se

ladd_____   t_____tle   ch_____ch   y_____d

th_____d   sp_____kle   n_____se   lett_____

j_____k   f_____ty   n_____th   c_____cle

50

Directions: Complete the sentences, using the words in the list.

Complete each sentence, using a word from the list.

1. Gert can blow the big _____.   whirls

2. The wind _____ the leaves about.   hurt

3. Carlos was not _____ in the car accident.   store

4. The North _____ can guide you at night.   horn

5. A mother bird is never _____ away from her nest.   corn

6. There is a _____ at the end of my street.   fur

7. The chickens ate all the _____ in the box.   Star

8. My little sister likes me to _____ her hair.   far

9. I am not allowed to play outdoors when it is _____.   purple

10. The color _____ is sometimes called violet.   curl

11. Martha is now in the _____ grade.   dark

12. My cat's _____ gets thicker in cold weather.   ferns

13. Mom grows pretty _____ in her garden.   for

14. I am looking _____ the pen that I lost this morning. third

51

Directions: In the first section, draw a ring around the **AR**, **OR**, **IR**, **UR**, or **ER** in each word, and write another word, using the same vowel sound. On the lines in the second section, write sentences using words from the list.

Draw a ring around the **ar**, **or**, **ir**, **ur**, or **er** in these words, and then write new words.

f i r	f_____st		b u r n	c_____l
l e t t e r	butt_____		c o r n	f_____
h u r t	n_____se		g i r l	f_____
d a r k	p_____t		s t a r	f_____
b o r n	c_____k		s p a r k l e	p_____k
t h i r d	d_____t		n e v e r	bett_____
b a r n	h_____m		p u r p l e	t_____tle

Complete each sentence, using a word from the list.

cord   storm   derby   start   nurse   market   birthday

1. Marge will _____ on her trip this morning.

2. Marvin tried to win first place in the _____.

3. The _____ looked at the cut on the girl's finger.

4. Carl and Norma drove during the big _____.

5. Here is a strong _____ to tie the parcel.

6. Mom needed some corn and oranges from the _____.

7. She received a purse and a card for her _____.

Directions: In the first section, read each sentence and draw a line under each word that contains **AR, OR, IR, UR,** or **ER.** In the second section, write the word you underlined in the first section.

Draw a line under each word that contains **ar, or, ir, ur,** or **er.**

1. Sandy sorted some Easter eggs and hid them under the porch.

2. Mom served Mrs. Brown a second piece of pie.

3. A marching band led the show horses into the circus ring.

4. Peter is finished with the pitchfork.

5. Roy will start with the children who are in the third grade.

6. Mr. Green found a purse in front of the church on Main Street.

7. The nurse forbade the little children to disturb Brad.

8. The little girl hung by her knees from the bar.

9. The tiny pet bird was thirsty.

10. A spark from the match fell on the curtain.

Write the words from the above sentences that contain **ar, or, ir, ur,** or **er.**

ir	er	ur	ar	or
_____	_____	_____	_____	_____
_____	_____	_____	_____	_____
_____	_____	_____	_____	_____
_____	_____	_____	_____	_____

53

Directions: In the first section, say each word and write the number of vowels you see and the number of vowel sounds you hear. In the second section, write the number of vowel sounds you hear and the number of syllables in each word.

Write the number of vowels seen and the number of vowel sounds heard.

	Vowels Seen	Vowel Sounds Heard		Vowels Seen	Vowel Sounds Heard
joke	_____	_____	so	_____	_____
miles	_____	_____	be	_____	_____
basket	_____	_____	strong	_____	_____
fish	_____	_____	bottom	_____	_____
oatmeal	_____	_____	each	_____	_____
teacup	_____	_____	plain	_____	_____

REMEMBER: If you hear one vowel sound in a word, it is a one-syllable word. If you hear two vowel sounds in a word, it is a two-syllable word.

Write the number of vowel sounds heard and the number of syllables.

	Vowel Sounds Heard	Syllables		Vowel Sounds Heard	Syllables
leaves	_____	_____	paint	_____	_____
ceiling	_____	_____	music	_____	_____
shine	_____	_____	Monday	_____	_____
slipper	_____	_____	crossroads	_____	_____
cave	_____	_____	please	_____	_____
rabbit	_____	_____	happy	_____	_____

Directions: Write the number of syllables in each word.

REMEMBER:	If you hear one vowel sound in a word, the word has one syllable.
	If you hear two vowel sounds in a word, the word has two syllables.

include _____	prison _____	freedom _____
clock _____	cranky _____	sprain _____
string _____	grin _____	story _____
clay _____	snowslide _____	snowdrop _____
cricket _____	snapshot _____	frosty _____
street _____	spoken _____	swept _____
strap _____	springtime _____	blame _____
squirrel _____	letter _____	mother _____
breeze _____	storeroom _____	grandson _____
blackbird _____	asked _____	frost _____
creep _____	plant _____	snappy _____
classroom _____	flower _____	purple _____
skates _____	grassy _____	dropped _____
brush _____	branch _____	faster _____
float _____	cross _____	fresh _____

Directions: In the first section, write the number of syllables in each word. In the second section, write the name of each picture, write the number of syllables in its name, and color the picture.

REMEMBER: The letters **ar**, **or**, **ir**, **ur**, and **er** contain one vowel sound.
A word has as many syllables as it has vowel sounds.

Write the number of syllables in each word.

shortly	_____	factory	_____	dirty	_____	pepper	_____
popcorn	_____	thirsty	_____	storm	_____	army	_____
Saturday	_____	carpet	_____	dangerous	_____	pitchfork	_____
part	_____	fern	_____	yesterday	_____	cord	_____
turkey	_____	feather	_____	carving	_____	chirping	_____
garden	_____	thunder	_____	father	_____	forty	_____
corner	_____	march	_____	jerk	_____	gingerbread	_____
jar	_____	short	_____	curve	_____	farmer	_____
fifty	_____	turnip	_____	morning	_____	purse	_____
carton	_____	dart	_____	person	_____	under	_____
clerk	_____	story	_____	farm	_____	dessert	_____

Write the name of each picture and the number of syllables. Color the pictures.

_____ _____   _____ _____   _____ _____

Directions: In each box make a word by matching a syllable in the first column to a syllable in the second column. Write the words on the lines.

bas	per	_____	la	ate	_____
lan	ket	_____	cre	zy	_____
pa	ney	_____	bun	form	_____
chim	tern	_____	plat	ny	_____
den	teen	_____	rab	den	_____
mon	ger	_____	trum	yon	_____
fif	tist	_____	hid	bit	_____
fin	key	_____	can	pet	_____
ten	plete	_____	kit	pet	_____
sup	der	_____	car	ven	_____
pan	try	_____	six	ten	_____
com	per	_____	e	teen	_____
teach	ed	_____	my	cret	_____
af	ny	_____	se	self	_____
po	ter	_____	bit	ger	_____
paint	ing	_____	gin	ten	_____

Directions: Write the number of syllables in each word.

thunder	_____	worm	_____	person	_____
march	_____	turnip	_____	snapshot	_____
blush	_____	danger	_____	float	_____
father	_____	dirty	_____	pitchfork	_____
part	_____	purse	_____	bedding	_____
play	_____	children	_____	wonderful	_____
umbrella	_____	penny	_____	milkman	_____
blackboard	_____	something	_____	monkey	_____
cannon	_____	elephant	_____	derby	_____
morning	_____	green	_____	melon	_____
pocket	_____	smile	_____	Mom	_____
start	_____	corner	_____	boat	_____
street	_____	blame	_____	telephone	_____
prison	_____	squirrel	_____	yesterday	_____
finger	_____	turkey	_____	tractor	_____
surprise	_____	funny	_____	work	_____
airplane	_____	fell	_____	happy	_____

Directions: In the first section, add the suffixes **S**, **ED**, and **ING** to the words in the list. In the second section, write the root word for each of the words.

Form new words by adding the suffixes **s**, **ed**, and **ing**.

	s	ed	ing
play	_____	_____	_____
jump	_____	_____	_____
pick	_____	_____	_____
clean	_____	_____	_____
help	_____	_____	_____
learn	_____	_____	_____
cook	_____	_____	_____

REMEMBER: The word to which a suffix is added is called the ROOT WORD.

Write the root word for each of the following words.

started	_____	opening	_____
lifts	_____	makes	_____
washed	_____	cleaned	_____
picked	_____	burns	_____
spelling	_____	stacked	_____
caps	_____	cooking	_____
dressed	_____	hats	_____

Directions: In the first two exercises, form new words by adding the suffixes. In the third exercise, write the root word for each word.

Form new words by adding the suffixes **er**, **est**, **ly**, and **ness**.

	er	est	ly	ness
sick	_____	_____	_____	_____
neat	_____	_____	_____	_____
loud	_____	_____	_____	_____
quick	_____	_____	_____	_____

Form new words by adding the suffixes **ful** and **less**.

	ful	less
care	_____	_____
thank	_____	_____
pain	_____	_____
hope	_____	_____

Write the root word for each of the following words.

kindness	_____	gladly	_____
smaller	_____	harmless	_____
coldest	_____	spoonful	_____
useful	_____	sadness	_____
homeless	_____	taller	_____

Directions: Read the rule and work the exercises.

REMEMBER: When a vowel ends in silent **e**, drop the **e** before adding a suffix that begins with a vowel.

Form new words by adding the suffixes **es**, **ed**, and **ing**.

	es	ed	ing
hike			
skate			
receive			
rake			

Form new words by adding the suffixes **er** and **est**.

	er	est
fine		
ripe		
cute		
pure		

Write the root word for each of the following words.

taking		hiding	
shining		chased	
wiper		used	
smiles		bakes	

61

Directions: Review the rule for adding suffixes to words ending in **E**. In the first exercise, complete the sentences. In the second exercise, draw a ring around each word that has a suffix, and write its root word.

Complete the sentences, adding the correct suffix to the given word.

1. Paul is _____ a letter to his friend.   write

2. The girls are _____ at the pond.   skate

3. The brother is a good _____.   dance

4. Scott _____ us to his birthday party.   invite

5. Pam is _____ in the new house.   live

6. The children have _____ pictures in the book.   paste

7. The tall boy is _____ the flag.   raise

Draw a ring around each word with a suffix, and write its root word.

1. We are baking a date cake for the party.   _____

2. We saved our money to spend at the circus.   _____

3. Sue has new skates.   _____

4. Bill's puppy is cuter than mine.   _____

5. Joan is riding her new pony.   _____

6. Carl smiled as he told the joke.   _____

7. Jody ate the ripest banana.   _____

Directions: Study the rule and work the exercises.

REMEMBER: When a word ends in a single consonant preceded by a short vowel sound, usually double the consonant before adding a suffix that begins with a vowel.

Draw a ring around each word that ends in a single consonant. Add the suffixes **ed** and **ing** to each word in the list.

	ed	ing
tag	_____	_____
rip	_____	_____
jump	_____	_____
nap	_____	_____

Draw a ring around each word that ends in a single consonant. Add the suffixes **er** and **est** to each word in the list.

	er	est
big	_____	_____
fat	_____	_____
cold	_____	_____
hot	_____	_____

Draw a ring around each word with a suffix, and write its root word on the line.

1. The bird tapped the tree with his beak. _____

2. The robber was seen by the police. _____

3. She was scrubbing the floor when the prince saw her. _____

4. The rock skipped along on top of the water. _____

Directions: In the first section, complete each sentence by adding the correct suffix to the given word. In the second section, write the root word for each word.

Complete the sentences, adding the correct suffix to the given word.

1. The girls were _____ from the school yard.   run

2. The monkey was _____ and begging for peanuts.   sit

3. The car _____ suddenly as it hit the pole.   stop

4. Peter _____ the dog and gave him a bone.   pet

5. Mom is _____ the fancy cake.   cut

6. Mary _____ her mother to take her shopping.   beg

7. Who was the _____ in the big race?   win

8. Porky was the _____ pig I ever saw.   fat

Write the root word for each of the following words.

shopper _____   swimmer _____

tagged _____   stopper _____

tipping _____   batted _____

dripping _____   rubbed _____

chopper _____   tapped _____

batting _____   bigger _____

quitting _____   hopping _____

hitting _____   biggest _____

Directions: Review the rules for adding suffixes to root words. Add the given suffixes to the words in the exercises below.

Add suffixes to form new words.

	s or **es**	**ed**	**ing**
like	_____	_____	_____
jump	_____	_____	_____
bat	_____	_____	_____
pick	_____	_____	_____
love	_____	_____	_____

	ful	**less**
harm	_____	_____
pain	_____	_____
hope	_____	_____

	er	**est**	**ly**	**ness**
sick	_____	_____	_____	_____
fair	_____	_____	_____	_____
flat	_____	_____	_____	_____
short	_____	_____	_____	_____
quick	_____	_____	_____	_____
neat	_____	_____	_____	_____

Directions: In the first exercise, read the rules carefully. Write the numeral of the rule used in adding a suffix to each word. Then in the second exercise, complete the sentences.

Which rule would you use?

1. When a word ends in a double consonant, we add the suffix.

2. When a word ends in a silent **e**, we drop the **e** before adding a suffix that begins with a vowel.

3. When a word ends in a single consonant preceded by a short-vowel sound, we usually double the consonant before adding a suffix that begins with a vowel.

paste _____   pick _____   pin _____   rake _____

run _____   plan _____   shop _____   hunt _____

jump _____   hop _____   help _____   like _____

make _____   fill _____   bake _____   sit _____

Complete each sentence, adding the correct suffix to the given word.

1. Dennis is _____ us some ginger cookies.   bake

2. Mom and Greg are _____ down the street.   jog

3. Mr. White just finished _____ our house.   paint

4. Dad _____ Mr. White yesterday.   help

5. Do you want to go _____ with Dad today?   shop

6. The baby _____ cannot come over today.   sit

7. We _____ Meg to take us to the circus.   beg

8. Maria is a _____ in the choir.   sing

Directions: Draw a ring around each suffix, and write the root word on the line.

brighter	_____	fearless	_____	filled	_____
horses	_____	falling	_____	grows	_____
cupful	_____	runner	_____	hiker	_____
wonderful	_____	helpful	_____	takes	_____
quickly	_____	wished	_____	restful	_____
greater	_____	talked	_____	begged	_____
harmful	_____	sleeping	_____	player	_____
picked	_____	slipped	_____	tapped	_____
dancer	_____	fences	_____	neatness	_____
lovely	_____	helpless	_____	darker	_____
trying	_____	careless	_____	whitest	_____
kindness	_____	climbed	_____	spoonful	_____
feeding	_____	catcher	_____	neatly	_____
creamer	_____	homeless	_____	quickest	_____
plates	_____	bigger	_____	jumping	_____
hopped	_____	baker	_____	fastest	_____
friendly	_____	rolling	_____	runner	_____

Directions: In the first section, make a new word by adding the suffix **Y** to each word in the list. In the second section, complete each sentence by finding the correct word, adding the suffix **Y**, and writing the new word in the space.

Form new words by adding the suffix **y**.

sleep _____   frost _____

rain _____   thirst _____

air _____   dust _____

crank _____   rock _____

dream _____   lump _____

Complete the sentences, adding the suffix **y** to the correct word from the list.

1. My little sister has _____ hair.   wind

2. We gave the _____ man a drink.   curl

3. It was so _____ that my hat blew off.   thirst

4. We get out our sleds on _____ days.   squeak

5. My bedroom has a _____ door.   snow

6. Sally worked the _____ puzzle.   health

7. Pete stepped on a _____ nail.   trick

8. Tommy is a very _____ baby.   rust

9. Gerry lives on a very _____ street.   stick

10. The sun made the candy soft and _____.   bump

Directions: In the first section, write the root word for each word in column 1. In the second section, complete the sentences.

REMEMBER: When a word ends in a silent **e**, drop the **e** before adding a suffix that begins with a vowel.

Find a root word in Column 2 that matches a word in Column 1. Write the root on the line.

1	2	1	2
washable _____	hard	soften _____	blame
harden _____	clean	sinkable _____	soft
darken _____	wash	blamable _____	bright
cleanable _____	like	brighten _____	sink
likable _____	dark	burnable _____	love
breakable _____	break	lovable _____	burn

Complete each sentence, using a word from the first section.

1. When we can wash something, we say it is _____.

2. When we can break something, we say it is _____.

3. When we can sink something, we say it is _____.

4. When we can like something, we say it is _____.

5. When we cause something to be dark, we _____ it.

6. When we cause something to be soft, we _____ it.

7. When we cause something to be bright, we _____ it.

69

Directions: Draw a ring around each suffix asked for, and write the root word on the line.

Suffix **y**

1. Tim was lucky in winning the prize. _____

2. The sun had melted the tar, and it was sticky. _____

3. The Rocky Mountains are in the West. _____

4. It had not rained, so the playground was dusty. _____

5. It was a cold and frosty morning. _____

Suffix **en**

1. John and Anna began to straighten the room. _____

2. Miss Gray said, "Please darken the room." _____

3. The blacksmith beat the hot iron to harden it. _____

4. Tom used a spotlight to brighten the stage. _____

5. Kate did not want to frighten Jill. _____

Suffix **able**

1. Jimmy's baseball suit is washable. _____

2. The scoutmaster was very likable. _____

3. The clothing that was wearable was saved. _____

4. The small boat was not sinkable. _____

5. The boy's handwriting was readable. _____

Directions: Read the rules carefully, and work the exercises.

REMEMBER: If a word ends in **y** preceded by a consonant, change the **y** to **i** and add the suffix **es**.
If a word ends in **y** preceded by a vowel, just add the suffix **s**.

Make each word mean more than one.

cherry _____   lily _____   party _____

fairy _____   fly _____   story _____

Underline each word that means more than one, and write its root word.

1. The puppies spilled the bowl of milk.   _____

2. Lucy watched the babies in the playpen.   _____

3. The field was full of white daisies.   _____

4. A plate of fresh cookies lay on the table.   _____

Make each word mean more than one.

boy _____   chimney_____   toy _____

turkey _____ day _____   ray _____

Underline each word that means more than one, and write its root word.

1. Peggy fed the monkeys at the zoo.   _____

2. His mother set out trays of food.   _____

3. The blue jays stayed all winter.   _____

Directions: Read the rule and work the exercises.

> **REMEMBER:** If a word ends in **ss**, **x**, **ch**, or **sh**, usually add the suffix **es** to make it mean more than one.

Make each word mean more than one.

cross _____	glass _____	match _____
box _____	six _____	fish _____
dress _____	church _____	brush _____
ax _____	dish _____	watch _____

Underline each word meaning more than one, and write its root word on the line.

1. One of Kim's wishes was to have a new bicycle. _____

2. The firefighter told me never to play with matches. _____

3. Jim helps his dad with the dishes. _____

4. The boxes were stacked high under the tree. _____

5. Grandma's dresses were in the closet. _____

6. The forest near the camp was full of foxes. _____

7. Nick's guesses were always correct. _____

8. The little girl looked at the pretty watches. _____

9. The cowboy had worked on ranches in Mexico. _____

10. The little boy had patches on his shirt. _____

Directions: Read the rule. In the first section, write each word, making it mean more than one. In the second section, underline each word that means more than one, and write its root word.

REMEMBER: In words ending in **f** or **fe**, usually change the **f** or **fe** to **v** before adding the suffix **es**.

Make each word mean more than one.

leaf _____   knife _____   half _____

calf _____   shelf _____   wife _____

wolf _____   elf _____   life _____

Underline each word that means more than one, and write its root word on the line.

1. A plant's leaves help make food for it.   _____

2. Jan uses knives to carve wood.   _____

3. The cow led the calves to the new pasture.   _____

4. At night the wolves came down the hill.   _____

5. The boy built shelves over his workbench.   _____

6. Each of the elves had his special work to do.   _____

7. The baker wrapped the loaves in wax paper.   _____

8. The guardrail was built to save lives.   _____

9. The wives in that neighborhood started
    a jogging club.   _____

10. We went to the barn to see the new calves.   _____

73

LESSON 28: REVIEWING SUFFIX -ES WITH WORDS ENDING IN SS, X, SH, F, AND FE

Directions: Review the rules. In the first section, write each word, making it mean more than one. In the second section, underline the word in each sentence that means more than one, and write its root word.

Make each word mean more than one.

watch _____ wish _____ wax _____

class _____ half _____ dress _____

fox _____ wife _____ kiss _____

Underline each word that means more than one, and write its root word on the line.

1. The calves won first prize at the county fair. _____

2. Mary Jane visited the stores in town. _____

3. The new doll has three dresses. _____

4. The kind old man sharpened Mom's knives. _____

5. Leaves change color in the autumn. _____

6. Dad painted the kitchen shelves. _____

7. May carried the boxes to the barn for Dad. _____

8. Please, bring the dishes over to the sink. _____

9. The elves lived under the stump of an old tree. _____

10. It is not safe to play with matches. _____

11. The chimney sweep used brushes to clean the fireplace. _____

12. We took the loaves of bread from the oven. _____

Directions: In the first section, complete each sentence by using a word from the list. In the second section, separate the words from the list in the first section into syllables.

Complete the sentences.

1. The sky became _____, then it rained.   greatest

2. He was the _____ pitcher of all time.   careless

3. Many accidents are caused by _____ drivers.   neatness

4. Grace was _____ at the clown.   cloudy

5. My report card has a good mark for _____.   playful

6. Tony helped Grandpa pick the _____.   laughing

7. The _____ puppy rolled over on his side.   peaches

8. Sue said the flowers we brought were _____.   brighten

9. Dad used yellow paint to _____ the room.   useful

10. A map is very _____ in taking a trip.   lovely

11. The storm left many families _____.   slowly

12. The parade moved down the street _____.   homeless

Separate the words into syllables.

_____ _____ _____ _____

_____ _____ _____ _____

_____ _____ _____ _____

75

Directions: Separate each word into syllables, using hyphens.

REMEMBER: A suffix containing a vowel sound forms a syllable in itself.

playing	_____	training	_____
lighten	_____	eating	_____
spoonful	_____	homeless	_____
gladly	_____	blooming	_____
needed	_____	careful	_____
playful	_____	laughing	_____
cheerful	_____	patches	_____
lovely	_____	painted	_____
shining	_____	wiper	_____
loudest	_____	snowy	_____
useless	_____	hopeful	_____
peaches	_____	rainy	_____
darkness	_____	neatness	_____
slowly	_____	brighten	_____
waiting	_____	cloudy	_____
careless	_____	useful	_____

_____

Directions: Write the number of syllables in each word.

knives	_____	plays	_____	shelves	_____
boxes	_____	churches	_____	tagging	_____
cleaned	_____	parties	_____	jumped	_____
hopeful	_____	thirsty	_____	loving	_____
loudly	_____	chimneys	_____	sleepy	_____
painful	_____	darken	_____	sickness	_____
receiving	_____	foxes	_____	hiking	_____
wives	_____	days	_____	harmless	_____
purest	_____	glasses	_____	leaves	_____
shining	_____	running	_____	gladly	_____
cherries	_____	cooking	_____	patches	_____
begging	_____	rolling	_____	wolves	_____
skated	_____	weakest	_____	snowy	_____
straighten	_____	homeless	_____	smoothest	_____
wiper	_____	axes	_____	picked	_____
turkeys	_____	whitest	_____	sinkable	_____
breakable	_____	raking	_____	daisies	_____

77

Directions: Read the rule, and say the name of each picture. Then complete each sentence below, using a word from the list at the right.

REMEMBER: If a one-part word or syllable has two vowels, the first vowel usually stands for a long sound and the second is silent.

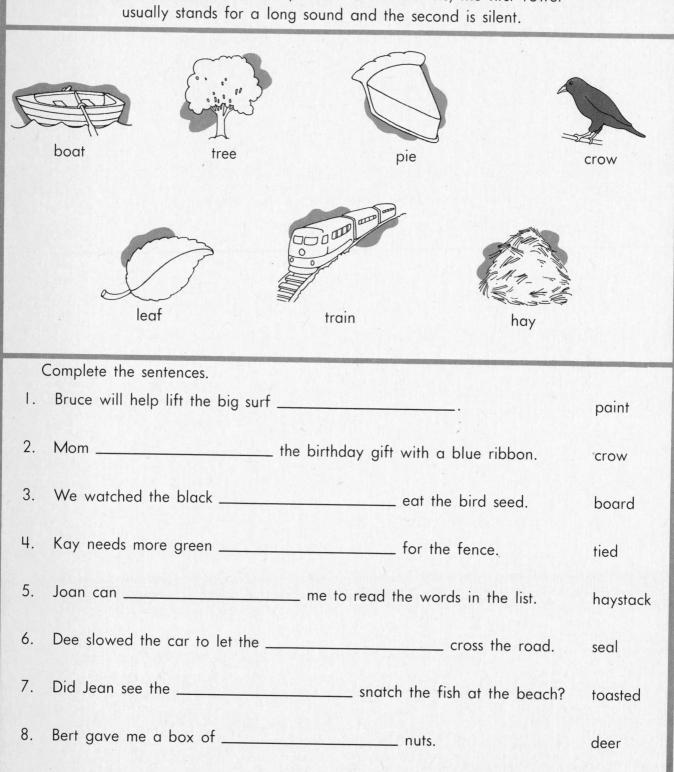

boat   tree   pie   crow

leaf   train   hay

Complete the sentences.

1. Bruce will help lift the big surf _____.   paint

2. Mom _____ the birthday gift with a blue ribbon.   crow

3. We watched the black _____ eat the bird seed.   board

4. Kay needs more green _____ for the fence.   tied

5. Joan can _____ me to read the words in the list.   haystack

6. Dee slowed the car to let the _____ cross the road.   seal

7. Did Jean see the _____ snatch the fish at the beach?   toasted

8. Bert gave me a box of _____ nuts.   deer

9. Dean lay in the _____ and slept all day.   teach

Directions: Read the sentences. Draw a ring around each word that contains a regular double vowel. Then write the words on the lines at the bottom of the page.

1. Mark raked the leaves into a pile for Dad.

2. The men used a trailer to move the furniture.

3. Jeff tried on his dad's coat and tie.

4. The team will play baseball at Grove Park.

5. Please pass the plate of grapes to Greg.

6. During the storm the hail beat hard on the window.

7. The dust from the trail made the horses thirsty.

8. Ask Jay to get the hose for Dad.

9. The pail and mops are kept in the side closet.

10. Tommy got his feet wet on the boat ride.

11. We had three minutes to finish the test.

12. Dave saw a toad and a snail on the rock.

13. Dad painted the walls a pretty shade of pink.

14. We all got a new toaster for Christmas.

_____ _____ _____

_____ _____ _____

_____ _____ _____

_____ _____ _____

_____ _____ _____

Directions: In the first section, draw a ring around the double vowel that is needed to complete the unfinished word in each sentence, and write it in the space. In the second section, answer each riddle with a word that contains the given double vowel.

1. Keith played in the sn_____ all day.   ie   ow   oa

2. How do you f_____l today?   ee   oa   ay

3. Jack sat down in his s_____t.   ay   ea   oa

4. Billy made a new s_____l for his toy boat.   ai   oa   ow

5. The little dog wagged his t_____l.   oa   ai   ea

6. We were all hungry for pumpkin p_____.   ay   ie   ai

7. The man ran to catch the tr_____n.   oa   ee   ai

8. The glass of milk is on the tr_____.   ay   ea   oa

9. I always have t_____st for breakfast.   ee   ai   oa

10. The old wagon has lost a wh_____l.   ai   ee   ay

11. You have to kn_____l when you scrub the floor.   ie   oa   ee

Answer each riddle with a word that contains the given double vowel.

1. Something to sail in.   oa   _____

2. Something we do to shoe strings.   ie   _____

3. Something that runs on tracks.   ai   _____

4. Something a rooster can do.   ow   _____

5. Something we do at recess.   ay   _____

6. Something that means the same as "talk." ea   _____

80

Directions: Read about the irregular double vowels **OO** and **EA**. Draw a ring around each word that contains an irregular double vowel in the sentences below. Write the words in the correct columns.

book

tools

headline

Read the words under the pictures.

Sometimes <u>oo</u> has the sound of <u>oo</u> as we hear it in <u>book</u>. At other times, it has the sound of <u>oo</u> as we hear it in <u>tools</u>.

In most words <u>ea</u> has the sound of long <u>e</u>. Sometimes it has the sound of short <u>e</u> as in <u>headline</u>.

Draw a ring around each word that contains an irregular double vowel. Write the words in the correct columns.

1. The team was ready to play a good game.

2. Burt moved the heavy stool and stood on it.

3. One goose flew behind the others in the flock.

4. The mean old man shook his head and said, "Not now."

5. Look at the bread.

6. The snow on the roof was two feet deep by noontime.

<u>oo</u> as in <u>book</u>   <u>oo</u> as in <u>tools</u>   <u>ea</u> as in <u>headline</u>

_____   _____   _____

_____   _____   _____

_____   _____   _____

81

Directions: Read about the irregular double vowels **AU**, **AW**, and **EI**. Draw a ring around each word that contains an irregular double vowel in the sentences below. Write the words in the correct columns.

saw

auto

eight

Look at each picture, and say its name.

aw has the sound of aw as we hear it in saw.

au has the same sound as aw.

ei, in many words, has the sound of ei as we hear it in eight.

Draw a ring around each word that contains an irregular double vowel. Write the words in the correct columns.

1. The lawyer yawned as she waited to see Paul.

2. The driver crawled from the freight truck after the crash.

3. He was bleeding because a vein was cut below his knee.

4. The artist was drawing a picture of a sleigh and reindeer.

5. At the lake last August, an old sailor taught us to tie knots.

aw as in saw   au as in auto   ei as in eight

_____   _____   _____

_____   _____   _____

_____   _____   _____

_____   _____   _____

Directions: Draw a ring around each word containing an irregular double vowel. Write the words in the correct lists.

1. The water in the brook is cold even in August.

2. Howard shook the rugs and left them on the lawn.

3. The freight truck zoomed along the smooth road.

4. She held her breath and dove into the pool.

5. We put a hat with a feather on the snowman's head.

6. The farmer slowly hauled the straw into the barn.

7. The naughty boy stood in the corner.

8. They towed the broken sleigh to the blacksmith's shop.

9. Our neighbor's dog hurt his paw.

book	**moon**	**eight**
_____	_____	_____
_____	_____	_____
_____	_____	_____

thread	**saw**	**auto**
_____	_____	_____
_____	_____	_____
_____	_____	_____

Directions: Write a rhyming word having the same double vowel as the name of each picture. The given beginning letters will help you.

peach	hook	book	rain
bl_____	cr_____	br_____	br_____

broom	eight	crow	hay
gl_____	fr_____	sn_____	tr_____

saw	bread	goat	tree
str_____	thr_____	fl_____	thr_____

Directions: Find each regular and irregular double-vowel word in the sentences. Write the words in the correct columns.

1. Paul tried to throw the ball over the roof.

2. May ran up the road to meet Jill.

3. The children looked at the jar of cookies.

4. The weather was good for a sleigh ride.

5. The yellow boat hauled the cargo.

6. The rain and sleet beat on the windowpane.

7. Dad taught Dawn to measure with a ruler.

Regular   **Irregular**

_____   _____

_____   _____

_____   _____

_____   _____

_____   _____

_____   _____

_____   _____

_____   _____

85

Directions: Look at the pictures, and read about diphthongs. Then complete each sentence below, using a word from the list at the right.

REMEMBER: A DIPHTHONG is two vowels sounded so that both vowels can be heard blended together as one.

boy   coins   owl   scout   screw

Say the names of the first two pictures. The vowel sound <u>oy</u> in <u>boy</u> is the same as <u>oi</u> in <u>coins</u>. Say these words: <u>toy</u>, <u>enjoy</u>, <u>royal</u>, <u>boil</u>, <u>point</u>.

Say the names of the next two pictures. The vowel sound <u>ow</u> in <u>owl</u> is the same as <u>ou</u> in <u>scout</u>. Say these words: <u>how</u>, <u>town</u>, <u>found</u>, <u>house</u>.

Say the name of the last picture. The <u>ew</u> in words is usually sounded as it is in <u>stew</u> and <u>screw</u>. Say these words: <u>new</u>, <u>few</u>, <u>blew</u>, <u>threw</u>.

1. He lost the _____ that held the machine together.   royal

2. A _____ gathered at the new building's window.   screw

3. The queen can be head of the _____ family.   blouse

4. Janet wore her new skirt and _____ to school.   joined

5. The boys _____, "Help!" as they clung to the slippery cliff.   crowd

6. Dot _____ the Girl Scouts last summer.   boiled

7. The water _____ over the side of the kettle.   town

8. The mayor had the _____ decorated for the parade.   shouted

Directions: Complete the sentences in the first section. In the second section, draw a ring around the word in each row that does not have the same irregular double-vowel sound as the first word in the row.

Complete the sentences.

1. We had _____ for dinner last night.   oil

2. Dad has to put _____ into the machine.   noise

3. The _____ from the street kept us awake.   stew

4. The airplane _____ from New York to Paris.   enjoy

5. The children will _____ this exciting story.   owl

6. Roy formed the clay into a _____ ball.   crew

7. A new _____ of firemen came to replace the tired men.   flew

8. The _____ had big eyes and a short beak.   house

9. Sharon lives in the brick _____ across the street.   crown

10. John is the new _____ in our class.   round

11. The king wore his _____ on one side of his head.   boy

Draw a ring around the word that does not have the same irregular double-vowel sound as the first word in the row.

toy	Roy	jaw	enjoy	boy
loud	shout	moon	about	sound
now	snow	cow	crowd	how
owl	bowl	drown	town	crown
toil	spoil	boil	coil	yawn
house	out	mouse	book	blouse

87

Directions: Draw a ring around the correct word, and write it on the line.

1. The queen wore a golden _____.   crowd   crown

2. The children played in the _____.   horse   house

3. The brown can was full of _____.   oil   owl

4. The cheese was eaten by the _____.   mouth   mouse

5. We get milk from the _____.   cow   cloth

6. Roy fell down and hurt his _____.   shout   mouth

7. We tossed coins into the _____.   found   fountain

8. The rain came down and the wind _____.   blew   blow

9. Julie rode down to _____.   town   tone

10. Ted put the kettle on to _____.   bowl   boil

11. The carpenter needed just one more _____.   screw   scratch

12. Mary tore her new red _____.   block   blouse

13. Dad told the girls not to be _____.   noisy   choice

14. The flowers were full of _____.   dell   dew

15. We all like things that are _____.   new   now

16. Mom painted the window frames _____.   cow   brown

17. In autumn the leaves fall onto the _____.   ground   grown

Directions: Write the irregular double vowel on the first line. Then say each word, and write the number of syllables you hear on the second line.

naughty	_____	_____	cookies	_____	_____
bread	_____	_____	sleighing	_____	_____
drawing	_____	_____	taught	_____	_____
reindeer	_____	_____	because	_____	_____
claw	_____	_____	bloom	_____	_____
neighbor	_____	_____	vein	_____	_____
awning	_____	_____	eighty	_____	_____
lawn	_____	_____	noodle	_____	_____
goose	_____	_____	thread	_____	_____
weigh	_____	_____	bookcase	_____	_____
autumn	_____	_____	breakfast	_____	_____
shook	_____	_____	sweater	_____	_____
pool	_____	_____	pleasant	_____	_____
weather	_____	_____	August	_____	_____
leather	_____	_____	daughter	_____	_____
freight	_____	_____	woodwork	_____	_____
measure	_____	_____	ready	_____	_____

Directions: Read each word. Then write the number of vowels you see, the number of vowel sounds you hear, and the number of syllables.

	Vowels You See	Vowel Sounds Heard	Number of Syllables		Vowels You See	Vowel Sounds Heard	Number of Syllables
auto	___	___	___	woodpile	___	___	___
tool	___	___	___	instead	___	___	___
bread	___	___	___	neighborly	___	___	___
weigh	___	___	___	August	___	___	___
broom	___	___	___	headline	___	___	___
sweater	___	___	___	cookies	___	___	___
bookcase	___	___	___	pause	___	___	___
school	___	___	___	eighteen	___	___	___
reindeer	___	___	___	breakfast	___	___	___
spool	___	___	___	haunted	___	___	___
seize	___	___	___	receive	___	___	___
feather	___	___	___	goose	___	___	___
bedspread	___	___	___	strawberry	___	___	___
weighted	___	___	___	measure	___	___	___
woodpecker	___	___	___	raccoon	___	___	___
laundry	___	___	___	jigsaw	___	___	___

Directions: In the first section, write the number of syllables in the box next to each word. In the second section, write in the box the number of syllables in the name of each picture.

REMEMBER: A diphthong is never separated when breaking a word into syllables.

Say each word.
In the box, write the number of syllables you hear.

threw	spoiled	south
bounce	oilcan	joyful
voice	growl	flowers
chew	cloudy	hoist
join	jewelry	account
annoy	mousetrap	strew
oyster	ointment	boiling
stew	noiseless	pointed
broil	enjoy	toybox
unscrew	newspaper	mouth

Say each word. Then write the number of syllables in the box. Color the pictures.

mouse ☐   toybox ☐   flowers ☐

91

Directions: Say each word. Write the number of vowel sounds you hear in the first column and the number of syllables in the second column.

	Vowel Sounds Heard	Number of Syllables		Vowel Sounds Heard	Number of Syllables
morning	____	____	boiler	____	____
rabbit	____	____	bottom	____	____
parade	____	____	railway	____	____
umbrella	____	____	account	____	____
pudding	____	____	below	____	____
because	____	____	outline	____	____
light	____	____	washed	____	____
statue	____	____	thousand	____	____
fountain	____	____	art	____	____
mousetrap	____	____	mountain	____	____
cried	____	____	south	____	____
apron	____	____	lady	____	____
bouncing	____	____	little	____	____
pointing	____	____	spider	____	____
create	____	____	impossible	____	____

Directions: Read each question. Find the answer in the word list, and write it on the line.

bad	dollars	naughty	fall	fruit	autumn
clown	annoy	growl	draw	color	magician
flowers	leather	crumble	happy	fur	glad
join	coins	connect	automobile	hit	car

1. What two-syllable word is the season that leaves fall? _____

2. What two-syllable word do we call children who disobey? _____

3. What one-syllable word is someone who does funny tricks? _____

4. What one-syllable word tells how you feel when you are happy? _____

5. What two-syllable word is something that grows from seeds? _____

6. What one-syllable word is a form of money? _____

7. What one-syllable word means to make two things meet? _____

8. What four-syllable word is the name of something you ride in? _____

9. What one-syllable word is something we do during art period? _____

10. What one-syllable word tells what dogs do when they are angry? _____

11. What two-syllable word is something you should not do to others? _____

12. What two-syllable word is something made from the skin of some animals? _____

Directions: In the first exercise, complete the name of each picture. In the second exercise, draw a ring around each consonant digraph that appears in the word list.

REMEMBER: A CONSONANT DIGRAPH consists of two consonants that go together to make one sound.

Complete each name.

bru_____   _____ip   si_____   pat_____

ele_____ant   _____irty   _____ot   _____ite

Draw a ring around each consonant digraph.

scheme	wheel	kitchen	write
birthday	threw	nickel	peaches
north	finish	mother	rough
beneath	choke	knit	echo
know	chord	thick	farther
telephone	shake	wrist	chocolate
bothered	ticket	wheat	chorus
tough	sign	school	gnaw

Directions: Choose the correct word to complete each sentence.

Complete the sentences.

1. I had a _____ in my lunch.   patch   peach

2. Our kitchen door has a broken _____.   knob   knock

3. Can you answer the _____?   telephone Phil

4. Chuck has a bad _____.   rough   cough

5. The beaver will _____ at the tree trunk.   gnat   gnaw

6. My brother's name is _____.   Philip   Phyllis

7. The _____ is a very tiny bird.   wren   wrench

8. The _____ was high above the fence.   reign   sign

9. When will you go to _____?   school   schooner

10. Last summer I broke my _____.   rust   wrist

11. I will tie the rope with a _____.   knot   knit

12. I locked my bike in place with a _____.   chain   chin

13. The coach used a _____.   whistle   white

14. Dad fixed the pipe with a _____.   wrench   ranch

15. The princess wore a _____ of roses in   wrong   wreath
    her hair.

Directions: Complete the sentences in the exercise at the top of the page. In the exercise at the bottom, write the consonant digraph from each word on the line.

Complete the sentences.

1. I saw the largest _____ in the zoo.   cough

2. A tall man _____ at the door.   elephant

3. Use your handkerchief when you _____.   knocked

4. I am trying to be a good _____.   wheel

5. The _____ on my bicycle is broken.   knit

6. Grandma will _____ a sweater.   writer

7. Our baby likes to _____.   chorus

8. Place the _____ and fork on the table.   laugh

9. Let's sing the _____ of the song again.   knife

Write the consonant digraphs.

laugh _____   kitchen _____   Ralph _____

choice _____   wrong _____   tough _____

know _____   chord _____   sign _____

gnaw _____   knife _____   gnarl _____

telephone _____   wrist _____   echo _____

Kathy _____   elephant _____   chemical _____

Directions: Find the consonant digraph in each word in the list. Write the word in the first column, if its consonant digraph comes at the beginning; in the second column, if it comes in the middle; and in the third column, if it comes at the end.

beach	another	path	chin	elephant	sheep
dishes	brush	wheel	write	matches	white
whine	birthday	with	tough	brother	cough
peaches	know	wish	sign	together	mother
show	tooth	truth	finish	patch	watching
telephone	shout	teacher	chorus	shadow	wrist

Beginning	**Middle**	**End**
_____	_____	_____
_____	_____	_____
_____	_____	_____
_____	_____	_____
_____	_____	_____
_____	_____	_____
_____	_____	_____
_____	_____	_____
_____	_____	_____

Directions: Complete the unfinished word in each sentence by writing the correct consonant digraph on the line.

ph	kn	wr	gh	ch	gn

1. Mom talked to Mary over the _____one.

2. We had a good lau_____ about the joke.

3. Are you going to _____ite a letter to your brother?

4. On the door was a large si_____ that said Fresh Paint.

5. The twins clapped when the dol_____in performed tricks.

6. Yesterday Nick had the _____ong answer for the problem.

7. Dad carved the tomatoes with a large _____ife.

8. We watched the beaver _____aw on the trunk of the tree.

9. I have a friend whose name is _____ilip.

10. We have learned to read in s_____ool.

11. Do you _____ow how to jump rope?

12. All the toys were under the _____ristmas tree.

13. The boy caught a cold and now has a bad cou_____.

14. It is not safe to be rou_____ at play.

15. Mark received a new _____istwatch for his birthday.

16. The Little League players received a tro_____y.

Directions: Complete the unfinished word in each sentence by drawing a ring around the correct blend or consonant digraph and writing it on the line.

1. Two _____easants eat at our winter bird feeder.   ph   gn   kn

2. The boys are playing with their new _____iend.   fr   ch   tr

3. Baby cries when she wakes up from her _____eep.   sm   sl   str

4. Chris _____ote to Suki, a Japanese girl just her age.   gn   kn   wr

5. Do you help your father _____inkle the lawn?   sp   dr   spr

6. Rick gave his puppy a huge bone to _____aw.   gr   gn   gh

7. Did you ever step on your _____adow?   sc   st   sh

8. The squirrel ran into the hole in the _____ee.   sr   tr   fr

9. I mount my snapshots in a _____otograph album.   gh   ph   sh

10. Donald was playing _____en the bell rang.   wh   th   ch

11. My doll was _____enched in the rain.   dr   pr   sp

12. Nora did not _____ow how hard the wind was blowing.   gn   kn   wr

13. Phyllis did not know Judy's tele_____one number.   ph   wr   th

14. Chuck will _____estle with Randy in the gym.   wr   ph   kn

15. One of the Cub Scouts lost his new _____apsack.   kn   wh   wr

16. My baby sister likes to play with _____ocks.   dr   bl   sl

17. Frank took fresh cookies to _____ool.   sh   ch   sch

Directions: In the first section, draw a ring around the consonant digraph in each word. In the second section, draw a ring around each word containing a consonant digraph, and write the words on the lines.

Draw a ring around each consonant digraph.

sheep	match	caught	lunch	chorus
dishes	finish	elephant	these	each
knew	wren	sign	check	right
choke	this	punch	telephone	shelf
gnat	pinch	shut	thrush	third
shop	luck	church	truck	knee
wheel	throat	crush	whisper	thank
chart	chop	write	when	chicken

Draw a ring around each word containing a consonant digraph. Write the words on the lines.

1. I saw a chicken in a truck. _____ _____

2. A chart is on the shelf. _____ _____

3. Mother Wren saw a big cat. _____ _____

4. Nick signed his name. _____ _____

5. I can wash six dishes at one time. _____ _____

6. I had my wheels checked. _____ _____

7. Touch your knee. _____ _____

8. Where is a telephone? _____ _____

9. I know the elephant's name. _____ _____

10. He fished at night. _____ _____

Directions: In the top section, write the number of vowels, the number of vowel sounds, and the number of syllables in each word. In the bottom section, write the number of vowels and the number of vowel sounds in each two-syllable word.

Write the number of vowels, the number of vowel sounds, and the number of syllables.

	Vowels	Vowel Sounds	Syllables
kitchen	_____	_____	_____
children	_____	_____	_____
white	_____	_____	_____
something	_____	_____	_____
bookshelf	_____	_____	_____

Draw a ring around each two-syllable word, and write the number of vowels and the number of vowel sounds.

	Vowels	Vowel Sounds
1. The white hen has ten chickens.	_____	_____
2. The cat hid beneath the chair.	_____	_____
3. Did you complete the test yesterday?	_____	_____
4. They peeled the peaches and ate them.	_____	_____
5. He tossed me a balloon filled with air.	_____	_____
6. The choir sang the chorus.	_____	_____
7. Dad gave me a baseball.	_____	_____
8. Shoes can be made of leather.	_____	_____

Directions: In the first box under the name of each picture, write the number of vowels you see; in the second box, the number of vowel sounds you hear; and in the third box, the number of syllables.

fish	coins	sandwich	scout

chicks	elephant	kitten	crown

goose	truck	cherry	mouse

volcano	blanket	towel	poison

Directions: In the first section, complete each sentence by choosing a one-syllable word that has only one vowel. In the second section, read the rhyme and choose one-syllable words from the rhyme to complete the sentences.

Complete the sentences.

1. We have one _____ in our classroom.   chair   bed   flag

2. Kathy invited _____ girls to her party.   seven   four   six

3. In May there are _____ on the trees.   snow   buds   leaves

4. Dad bought a new bicycle for _____.   Joe   you   me

5. Joyce took her _____ for a walk.   sled   doll   poodle

6. Mother and Dad _____ to Florida.   drove   went   walked

7. We should _____ to do our work well.   try   strive   like

8. Charles _____ in the country.   lives   is   remains

9. Five _____ work in the store.   men   babies   boys

Read the poem and choose one-syllable words from it to complete the sentences.

Oh, the Jumping Jack man
  Is a funny, funny man.
He jumps and he jumps
  As fast as he can.

His arms jump out
  And his legs jump, too.
Mr. Jumping Jack man,
  How we love you!
      —Averil

1. A boy's name is _____.

2. The opposite of "slow" is _____.

3. The opposite of "woman" is _____.

4. "Us" means the same as _____.

5. "We" rhymes with _____.

6. "To hop" means to _____.

Directions: Read each word. Then write the number of vowels you see, the number of vowel sounds you hear, and the number of syllables in each word.

	Vowels Seen	Vowel Sounds	Syllables		Vowels Seen	Vowel Sounds	Syllables
caboose				goblin			
headache				alphabet			
telephone				sunshine			
machine				velvet			
blossom				telescope			
license				chipmunk			
donkey				engine			
basket				damage			
pancakes				tepee			
teapot				sandwich			
pilot				elephant			
album				china			
lonely				breeze			
picnic				padlock			
equality				baggage			
bonnet				beechnut			

Directions: Write the number of syllables in each word on the line next to it.

joy	___	jaw	___	pineapple	___	new	___	saw	___
gay	___	boy	___	beam	___	forest	___	dream	___
burrow	___	faint	___	walk	___	broom	___	headache	___
noise	___	law	___	now	___	teacher	___	cheat	___
house	___	hood	___	clown	___	marching	___	curve	___
found	___	doctor	___	coin	___	proud	___	lead	___
harm	___	awful	___	shook	___	chew	___	men	___
loud	___	party	___	hoop	___	fur	___	daughter	___
porch	___	goodness	___	breakfast	___	invite	___	strawberry	___
drowsy	___	chirp	___	head	___	cat	___	auto	___
leather	___	noisy	___	oyster	___	sun	___	rail	___
overcoat	___	maid	___	treetop	___	spend	___	rooster	___
mother	___	lad	___	swimming	___	scarlet	___	popcorn	___
log	___	alphabet	___	light	___	lantern	___	wall	___
face	___	real	___	table	___	rudder	___	boat	___
newspaper	___	gun	___	enjoy	___	saying	___	bird	___
steam	___	howling	___	car	___	team	___	six	___

Directions: Write the root words on the lines below.

> **REMEMBER:**
> A PREFIX is a syllable placed before a root word to change its meaning or form a new word.
> The prefixes **un** and **dis** usually mean **not**.
> Examples: **Dishonest** means **not honest**.
> **Unfair** means **not fair**.

displease	_____	unpin	_____
uncertain	_____	unfold	_____
disorder	_____	disappear	_____
distrust	_____	unsafe	_____
unfair	_____	unchain	_____
unhappy	_____	discolor	_____
dissatisfy	_____	untrue	_____
unfold	_____	disable	_____
disagree	_____	uncover	_____
unload	_____	uneven	_____
unseen	_____	discharge	_____
unpleasant	_____	unequal	_____
dislocate	_____	unfit	_____
disobey	_____	disunite	_____

Directions: Complete the second sentence in each exercise, making it say the opposite of the first sentence.

1. This man is unable to do the work.

   This man is _____ to do the work.

2. Dot is disobeying her father.

   Dot is _____ her father.

3. The men are unloading the truck.

   The men are _____ the truck.

4. Kathy dislikes mustard on her sandwich.

   Kathy _____ mustard on her sandwich.

5. Ned was unhappy in his new home.

   Ned was _____ in his new home.

6. Greg's report card displeased his father.

   Greg's report card _____ his father.

7. Susan was unhurt in the accident.

   Susan was _____ in the accident.

8. Bob Brown left his closet in disorder.

   Bob Brown left his closet in _____.

9. Mom untied the baby's shoes.

   Mom _____ the baby's shoes.

Directions: Write the root words on the lines below.

REMEMBER:

The prefix **re** usually means **do again**.
Example: **Repaint** means **paint again**.

The prefix **de** usually means **from**.
Example: **Depart** means **go away from**.

The prefix **ex** usually means **out of** or **from**.
Example: **Export** means **send out of**.

deform	_____	depart	_____
reread	_____	rewash	_____
defrost	_____	dethrone	_____
exchange	_____	retie	_____
express	_____	detour	_____
rebuild	_____	depress	_____
refill	_____	export	_____
derail	_____	refile	_____
reopen	_____	deplane	_____
rewrite	_____	redress	_____
retrace	_____	demerit	_____
redo	_____	rewrap	_____
reload	_____	reclaim	_____

Directions: In each section, complete each sentence by choosing the correct word from the list at the right.

1. Chet ruined his homework and had to _____ it.

    dishonest

2. A person who cheats is _____.

    rewrite

3. Ellen left the dishes _____.

    exchange

4. Bill was late, and had to _____ his supper.

    unwashed

5. Andy's new sweaters are too small, so he will _____ them.

    reheat

6. It is wrong to _____ your parents.

    defrost

7. I forgot the story, so I will _____ it sometime.

    expert

8. It is time to _____ the refrigerator.

    unhappy

9. Kim is an _____ ball player.

    disobey

10. Joan cried because she was _____.

    reread

11. Dad asked Kelly to _____ the joke.

    dislike

12. The girls set out to _____ the cave.

    unfair

13. The captain is _____ to his team.

    explore

14. The members of the team _____ him.

    rebuild

15. Exercise helps to _____ the muscles.

    retell

Directions: In the first section, write the root word for each word on the line next to it. In the second section, complete each sentence by choosing the correct word from the first section.

Write the root word.

dislike _____	refill _____	defrost _____
retell _____	unable _____	disobey _____
retrace _____	dishonest _____	untie _____
exchange _____	reopen _____	unwrap _____
unsafe _____	uncover _____	explain _____

Complete each sentence, using a word from the list above.

1. A person who tells lies is _____.

2. Pedro will _____ his pen with ink.

3. Carla will _____ her new T-shirt for a book.

4. We asked Dad to _____ the old story.

5. Jan is _____ to go with you today.

6. Miss Day was trying to _____ the problem to David.

7. I _____ having to go to bed early.

8. We will _____ the refrigerator.

9. The museum is closed, but it will _____ next week.

10. My little brother can _____ his shoes.

Directions: Look closely at the definitions below. Read each word in the list, and write the prefix, the root word, and the suffix.

A **prefix** is a syllable placed before a root word to change its meaning.	A **root word** is a word to which a prefix or a suffix may be added to change its meaning.	A **suffix** is a letter or a syllable placed at the end of a root word to change its meaning.

	prefix	root word	suffix
rebuilding	_____	_____	_____
recovered	_____	_____	_____
unkindly	_____	_____	_____
uncomfortable	_____	_____	_____
unhappiness	_____	_____	_____
discovers	_____	_____	_____
unlocking	_____	_____	_____
displeasing	_____	_____	_____
unpacking	_____	_____	_____
explaining	_____	_____	_____
derailed	_____	_____	_____
repainting	_____	_____	_____

Directions: Rewrite each word, placing a hyphen between the prefix and the root word.

REMEMBER: A prefix is a syllable in itself.

displease	_____	unkind	_____
return	_____	detour	_____
disown	_____	reread	_____
untie	_____	unscrew	_____
rewrite	_____	derail	_____
unpin	_____	renew	_____
replace	_____	explain	_____
unlike	_____	repaint	_____
unfair	_____	discharge	_____
exclaim	_____	unfold	_____
dislike	_____	rebuild	_____
undress	_____	exchange	_____
depart	_____	unpaid	_____
deform	_____	distract	_____
express	_____	display	_____

Directions: In the first section, complete each sentence by choosing the correct word from the list. In the second section, write the words from the list in syllables, using hyphens.

Complete the sentences.

1. Kay had to _____ why she was late.   rewrite

2. Do you _____ rainy weather?   renew

3. Bring a written _____ when you are absent.   decay

4. I will have to _____ my library book.   excuse

5. My teeth may _____ if I eat too much candy.   dislike

6. Judy had to _____ her letter.   explain

7. Mrs. Lang will _____ the best papers on the board.   depend

8. The children helped the farmer _____ the truck.   repainted

9. Your grades _____ upon the kind of work you do.   unfold

10. Please _____ your napkin carefully.   repave

11. The workers had to _____ the streets.   display

12. Our kitchen will be _____ .   unload

Divide the words into syllables, using hyphens.

_____   _____   _____

_____   _____   _____

_____   _____   _____

_____   _____   _____

Directions: Separate the words into syllables, using hyphens.

> **REMEMBER:** A suffix is a syllable in itself if it contains a vowel sound.

sleepless	_____	careless	_____
homeless	_____	kindness	_____
needed	_____	colder	_____
walking	_____	loudest	_____
newest	_____	landed	_____
flying	_____	greatest	_____
cupful	_____	fearless	_____
kindly	_____	making	_____
playing	_____	warmer	_____
reading	_____	boneless	_____
gladly	_____	sadly	_____
boxes	_____	peaches	_____
helpless	_____	safely	_____
healthful	_____	saying	_____
rested	_____	dampness	_____

Directions: Separate the words into syllables, using hyphens.

> **REMEMBER:** A suffix is a syllable in itself if it contains a vowel sound.
> A prefix is a syllable in itself.

playing	_____	loudest	_____
disclose	_____	softly	_____
displease	_____	harmless	_____
spoonful	_____	unkind	_____
unknown	_____	dislike	_____
colder	_____	sweeten	_____
careful	_____	needed	_____
explain	_____	slowly	_____
gladly	_____	slower	_____
retell	_____	express	_____
useless	_____	invented	_____
deform	_____	peaches	_____
safely	_____	unhandy	_____
looking	_____	unwilling	_____
unsafe	_____	return	_____

Directions: Separate the words into syllables, using hyphens.

painted _____	renew _____
careless _____	darkness _____
expanded _____	disclose _____
smoothly _____	looking _____
carefully _____	defeat _____
fastest _____	wisely _____
exchange _____	remaining _____
spoonful _____	unpacking _____
mixes _____	unknown _____
unpainted _____	peaches _____
helpful _____	truthfulness _____
greener _____	loudest _____
unwisely _____	charming _____
unwilling _____	catches _____
decidedly _____	resharpen _____
unseen _____	unkindly _____
extending _____	loosely _____

LESSON 44: TEST: RECOGNIZING SYLLABLES IN WORDS CONTAINING PREFIXES AND SUFFIXES

Directions: Draw a ring around each word that has a prefix or a suffix. Then separate the word into syllables, using hyphens.

1. Mark is helpful at home. _____

2. We must not be so careless with our money. _____

3. Tony reread the book over and over. _____

4. Vicky discarded an ace and lost the game. _____

5. The log is big enough to derail the train. _____

6. Please walk quickly to the door. _____

7. That is the most relaxing chair to sit in. _____

8. Miss Jones will explain our work to us. _____

9. Judy and Peggy had to unpack the suitcase. _____

10. The sheriff drove swiftly to the hospital. _____

11. Please return the storybook to this shelf. _____

12. The paint will dry to a smooth hardness. _____

13. Jean repainted her bedroom. _____

14. The cough medicine was distasteful. _____

15. The children were restless as they stood in line. _____

16. The guard saw the boy floating on the raft. _____

Directions: Read carefully about dividing words into syllables. In the exercise below, write each compound word, dividing it into syllables, using hyphens.

To recognize a long word that is new, we look for smaller words within the long word, or pronounce it syllable by syllable, listening to see if we can recognize it as a word we have used or heard before. To do this we must know how to divide a word into syllables.

Knowing how to divide a word into syllables is also useful in writing. When there is not enough room at the end of a line to write a long word, we can write some of its syllables on the first line and the rest of them on the next line. When we do this, we use a hyphen at the end of the first line to show that the word is not complete.

Rules for Syllabication:

RULE 1: A one-syllable word is never divided.

RULE 2: Divide a compound word between the words that make the compound word.

into	_____	doorman	_____
birthday	_____	cowboy	_____
rainbow	_____	inside	_____
tiptoe	_____	someone	_____
sidewalk	_____	sunshine	_____
tonight	_____	today	_____
dishpan	_____	highway	_____

Directions: In the first section, write each compound word, dividing it with a hyphen. In the second section, underline each compound word in the story, and divide each one by drawing a line through it.

Write each word, dividing it into syllables.

lifeboat	_____	clubhouse	_____
railway	_____	pancake	_____
airplane	_____	something	_____
milkman	_____	stairway	_____
cloakroom	_____	into	_____
forget	_____	popcorn	_____

Draw a line to divide each compound word.

Roundup Time

It was roundup time at Horseshoe Ranch. The cowhands stood outside the bunkhouse, listening to the foreman's orders. John had gone inside the storeroom to ask his grandfather to let him go. It would be his first roundup.

"You're a good horseback rider," said Grandfather. "You will make a good cowboy, too. Get your bedroll."

John slipped into his cowhide jacket, picked up his campfire outfit, and ran through the doorway. He went to the barnyard and saddled his chestnut mare, Blackfoot.

The cowmen rode all afternoon. At sundown they sat around the fireside and ate beefsteaks and flapjacks. Then all the grownups began to undo their bedrolls. John stayed beside the fire for a moment. He sat on a log and gazed at the stars. They were bright and clear. The small pinpoints of light glimmered in the cold night air.

Suddenly John saw a much larger blaze of light. The campfire had spread to the chuckwagon! John thought quickly. He knew that if the chuckwagon burned, the cowhands would be without food. John spotted the cook's flour sack near the wagon. Quickly he poured everything in the large flour sack on the fire. The fire went out.

John's grandpa ran up to him. He had seen how John's quick thinking had saved the day.

"Without you, all of our food would have been lost," he said. "You are a real cowboy, John. I'm glad you came with us."

Directions: Read the rules, and write the words, dividing them into syllables.

RULE 3: When a word has a suffix, divide the word between the root word and the suffix.

sailing _____ slower _____

darken _____ churches _____

thankful _____ sleeping _____

landed _____ safely _____

skating _____ foxes _____

loaded _____ fearless _____

hardness _____ smallest _____

RULE 4: When a word has a prefix, divide the word between the prefix and the root word.

unsafe _____ dislike _____

reread _____ unlock _____

distrust _____ misfit _____

rewrite _____ exchange _____

depart _____ unfair _____

express _____ depress _____

misprint _____ displease _____

Directions: Read the rule, and write the words, dividing them into syllables.

RULE 5: When two or more consonants come between two vowels in a word, the word is usually divided between the first two consonants.

picture	_____	sudden	_____
pencil	_____	number	_____
confess	_____	silver	_____
goblin	_____	Kansas	_____
forgave	_____	master	_____
basket	_____	finger	_____
admire	_____	invite	_____
princess	_____	kidnap	_____
complete	_____	doctor	_____
mistake	_____	riddle	_____
candy	_____	almost	_____
harbor	_____	chapter	_____
plenty	_____	surprise	_____
children	_____	dictate	_____
pilgrim	_____	butter	_____

Directions: In the first section, write the words, dividing them into syllables. In the second section, use the words to complete the sentences.

Divide each word into syllables.

magnet	_____	gallop	_____
blanket	_____	walnut	_____
servant	_____	hungry	_____
circus	_____	yellow	_____
picnic	_____	party	_____
puppy	_____	bottom	_____
button	_____	sudden	_____
chimney	_____	surprise	_____
shallow	_____	happen	_____

Complete each sentence, using a word from the section above.

1. Mom gave the _____ to Billy for a pet.

2. The _____ daisies looked lovely in the blue vase.

3. All of a _____ the whistle blew.

4. Mary sewed a _____ on her red sweater.

5. The birthday party was a _____ for Ted.

6. Susan rode her horse at a fast _____ .

Directions: Read the rules. Write each word, dividing it into syllables. Then write the numeral of the rule that you have used.

Rules for Syllabication:

1. A one-syllable word is never divided.
2. Divide a compound word between the words that make the compound word.
3. When a word has a suffix, divide the word between the root word and the suffix.
4. When a word has a prefix, divide the word between the prefix and the root word.
5. When two or more consonants come between two vowels in a word, the word is usually divided between the first two consonants.

---

airplane _____ ___

surprise _____ ___

homeless _____ ___

balloon _____ ___

smallest _____ ___

monkey _____ ___

donkey _____ ___

helping _____ ___

outdoors _____ ___

sudden _____ ___

later _____ ___

refresh _____ ___

quickly _____ ___

hungry _____ ___

hardness _____ ___

displease _____ ___

slowly _____ ___

safe _____ ___

curtain _____ ___

harmful _____ ___

backyard _____ ___

churches _____ ___

railroad _____ ___

circus _____ ___

LESSON 47: REVIEWING SYLLABICATION RULES

Directions: Divide each word into syllables. Write the rule you have used. You will find the rules on p. 123.

napkin _____   Rule: _____

_____

_____

home _____   Rule: _____

_____

_____

rosebud _____   Rule: _____

_____

_____

kindness _____   Rule: _____

_____

_____

dislike _____   Rule: _____

_____

_____

124 _____

Directions: Read the rule carefully. Write the words, dividing them into syllables. At the bottom of the page, write the new rule.

RULE 6: When a single consonant comes between two vowels in a word, the word is usually divided after the consonant if the first vowel is short.

Write each word, using a hyphen to divide it into syllables.

robin	_____	finish	_____
cabin	_____	river	_____
figure	_____	habit	_____
wagon	_____	clever	_____
tonic	_____	dragon	_____
travel	_____	magic	_____
palace	_____	visit	_____
statue	_____	shadow	_____
model	_____	pedal	_____

Write the new rule.

_____

_____

_____

Directions: In the first section, divide the words into syllables. In the second section, write the new rule.

RULE 7: When a single consonant comes between two vowels in a word, the word is usually divided before the consonant if the first vowel is long.

Write each word, dividing it into syllables.

lilac	_____	pirate	_____
polar	_____	pilot	_____
spider	_____	cozy	_____
frozen	_____	motel	_____
moment	_____	David	_____
lazy	_____	music	_____
pupil	_____	tiger	_____
lady	_____	broken	_____
famous	_____	paper	_____

Write the new rule.

_____

_____

_____

_____

Directions: In the first section, divide the words into syllables. In the second section, use the words to complete the sentences.

Write each word, dividing it into syllables.

polar   _____   tiger   _____

lilac   _____   climate   _____

pilot   _____   policeman   _____

spider   _____   cedar   _____

secret   _____   propeller   _____

Complete each sentence, using a word from the section above.

1. I am anxious to see the _____ when we go to the zoo.

2. The _____ is one of the sweetest-smelling flowers.

3. A _____ bear has a thick, warm coat of white fur.

4. Our clubhouse has a _____ entrance.

5. The crew had to fix the _____ on the plane.

6. We have three _____ trees on our front lawn.

7. The baby was afraid of the _____ crawling on the floor.

8. Mother wanted to go south because of the warm _____.

9. We reported the robbery to the _____.

10. The _____ will fly the plane to Mexico.

Directions: Write the vowel sound that you hear in the first syllable of each word. Then write the numeral of the rule that is used in dividing the word into syllables. In the last column, write the word, dividing it into syllables.

RULE 6: When a single consonant comes between two vowels in a word, the word is usually divided after the consonant if the first vowel is short.

RULE 7: When a single consonant comes between two vowels in a word, the word is usually divided before the consonant if the first vowel is long.

	Vowel Sound	Rule	Syllabication
moment	_____	___	_____
polar	_____	___	_____
magic	_____	___	_____
travel	_____	___	_____
minute	_____	___	_____
damage	_____	___	_____
finish	_____	___	_____
second	_____	___	_____
promise	_____	___	_____
Friday	_____	___	_____
medal	_____	___	_____
pilot	_____	___	_____
David	_____	___	_____

Directions: On the first line after each word, write the numeral of the rule that is used in dividing the word into syllables. On the second line, write the word, dividing it into syllables.

radar	___	_____
lemon	___	_____
hotel	___	_____
damage	___	_____
manage	___	_____
timid	___	_____
tiger	___	_____
dragon	___	_____
second	___	_____
pupil	___	_____
future	___	_____
magic	___	_____
broken	___	_____
begin	___	_____
never	___	_____
pirate	___	_____
travel	___	_____

cabin	___	_____
siren	___	_____
honest	___	_____
wagon	___	_____
label	___	_____
habit	___	_____
polar	___	_____
punish	___	_____
river	___	_____
melon	___	_____
duty	___	_____
nature	___	_____
moment	___	_____
pilot	___	_____
statue	___	_____
meter	___	_____
final	___	_____

Directions: On the first line after each word, write the numeral of the rule that is used in dividing the word into syllables. On the second line, write the word, dividing it into syllables.

Rules for Syllabication:

1. A one-syllable word is never divided.

2. Divide a compound word between the words that make the compound word.

3. When a word has a suffix, divide the word between the root word and the suffix.

4. When a word has a prefix, divide the word between the prefix and the root word.

5. When two or more consonants come between two vowels in a word, the word is usually divided between the first two consonants.

6. When a single consonant comes between two vowels in a word, the word is usually divided after the consonant if the first vowel is short.

7. When a single consonant comes between two vowels in a word, the word is usually divided before the consonant if the first vowel is long.

inside	___ _____	tragic	___ _____
explain	___ _____	happy	___ _____
stiffness	___ _____	first	___ _____
coin	___ _____	unjust	___ _____
melon	___ _____	dollhouse	___ _____
nature	___ _____	basket	___ _____
travel	___ _____	sweeper	___ _____
snowflake	___ _____	wishbone	___ _____
picnic	___ _____	pupil	___ _____

Directions: On the first line after each word, write the numeral of the rule that is used in dividing the word into syllables. On the second line, write the word, dividing it into syllables.

tablet	__	_____	hardness	__	_____
sunlight	__	_____	nine	__	_____
yellow	__	_____	slowly	__	_____
tiger	__	_____	polar	__	_____
tulip	__	_____	palace	__	_____
princess	__	_____	locate	__	_____
dragon	__	_____	pencil	__	_____
motel	__	_____	please	__	_____
depart	__	_____	renew	__	_____
stove	__	_____	dishpan	__	_____
sunshine	__	_____	useless	__	_____
cottage	__	_____	pepper	__	_____
wagon	__	_____	displease	__	_____
music	__	_____	pancake	__	_____
express	__	_____	thankful	__	_____
darken	__	_____	Friday	__	_____
shadow	__	_____	thunder	__	_____

Directions: In each word draw a ring around the vowel that is sounded by itself. Write the word, dividing it into syllables. After you have finished, write the new rule at the bottom of the page.

RULE 8: When a vowel is sounded alone in a word, it forms a syllable in itself.

Write each word, dividing it into syllables.

magazine _____   open _____

uniform _____   disagree _____

ahead _____   Canada _____

unit _____   telephone _____

disobey _____   alive _____

ocean _____   electric _____

against _____   manufacture _____

gasoline _____   Mexico _____

eternal _____   monument _____

Write the new rule.

_____

_____

_____

_____

Directions: In the first section, complete each sentence by using a word from the list at the right. In the second section, rewrite the words from the list in the first section, dividing them into syllables.

Complete the sentences.

1. Lucy likes to ride the _____ waves on her surfboard. disobey

2. A _____ was erected in honor of the hero. ocean

3. It is a crime to _____ the law. uniform

4. Mom read the story in a _____. monument

5. A soldier wears a _____. magazine

6. The giraffe is the tallest _____ at the zoo. gasoline

7. When we do not succeed we must try _____. catalog

8. My baby sister likes to _____ me. animal

9. The engines of most automobiles run on _____. again

10. Ted has a _____ of model airplanes. imitate

Write the words, dividing them into syllables.

_____   _____

_____   _____

_____   _____

_____   _____

_____   _____

Directions: Read the rule carefully. Write each word, dividing it into syllables. Then at the bottom of the page, write the new rule.

RULE 9: When two vowels come together in a word and are sounded separately, divide the word between the two vowels.

Write each word, dividing it into syllables.

giant	_____	radio	_____
polio	_____	lion	_____
rodeo	_____	diet	_____
radiator	_____	ruin	_____
graduate	_____	cruel	_____
dial	_____	pioneer	_____
usual	_____	poet	_____
science	_____	create	_____
poem	_____	idea	_____

Write the new rule.

_____

_____

_____

LESSON 50: RECOGNIZING SYLLABLES IN WORDS CONTAINING TWO VOWELS TOGETHER THAT ARE
SOUNDED SEPARATELY

Directions: Write each word, dividing it into syllables.

radio	_____	create	_____
piano	_____	rodeo	_____
diet	_____	dandelion	_____
diaper	_____	Ohio	_____
quiet	_____	science	_____
cruel	_____	idea	_____
graduate	_____	denial	_____
poem	_____	radiator	_____
lion	_____	fluid	_____
violin	_____	ruin	_____
violet	_____	trial	_____
giant	_____	theater	_____
guardian	_____	pioneer	_____
hyena	_____	realize	_____
ideal	_____	annual	_____
period	_____	warrior	_____

Directions: Write each word, dividing it into syllables.

RULE 8: When a vowel is sounded alone in a word, it forms a syllable in itself.

RULE 9: When two vowels come together in a word and are sounded separately, divide the word between the two vowels.

---

diet _____   create _____

above _____   ocean _____

poet _____   graduate _____

science _____   ruin _____

trial _____   melody _____

parakeet _____   duet _____

disagree _____   disobey _____

riot _____   gasoline _____

unopen _____   lion _____

ideal _____   magazine _____

president _____   pioneer _____

violets _____   gelatin _____

radio _____   hesitate _____

Directions: In the first section, write the words, dividing them into syllables. In the second section, use the words to complete the sentences.

Write each word, dividing it into syllables.

science	_____	Indian	_____
parakeets	_____	violin	_____
gasoline	_____	president	_____
giant	_____	lion	_____
melody	_____	ideal	_____

Complete each sentence, using a word from the section above.

1. Mary Ellen was elected _____ of our class.

2. That movie was about a cowboy and his _____ friend.

3. The _____ of the song was beautiful.

4. We are studying plants in our _____ class.

5. The circus had one _____ and six elephants.

6. Dad will buy _____ for the lawn mower.

7. At the top of the beanstalk Jack saw the _____.

8. The bandleader played the melody on his _____.

9. The pet shop has several pretty _____.

10. The weather was _____ for a picnic.

Directions: Read the rule carefully. Write each word, dividing it into syllables. Then at the bottom of the page, write the new rule.

RULE 10: When a word ends in **le** preceded by a consonant, divide the word before that consonant.

Write each word, dividing it into syllables.

turtle	_____	circle _____
puzzle	_____	purple _____
gentle	_____	bicycle _____
whistle	_____	needle _____
eagle	_____	riddle _____
maple	_____	people _____
pebble	_____	rattle _____
simple	_____	scramble _____
thistle	_____	temple _____

Write the new rule.

_____

_____

_____

Directions: Say the name of each picture, and write its name, dividing it into syllables.

Directions: In the first part, circle the **LE** words in the story, then write them on the lines, using hyphens for syllabication. In the second part, write the words in the list in syllables, using hyphens.

Read the story. Circle each word that contains **LE** preceded by a consonant. Then write each circled word with hyphens to divide it into syllables. Write each word only once.

A Day at the Lake

One day, Mary and her dad rode their bicycles to a small lake. They parked the bikes under a maple tree and headed for the boat dock.

"I'll show you how to handle a canoe," said Dad. "It's simple. You'll be able to do it in no time."

The man at the dock untied a dark purple canoe and held it against the dock. Mary and her dad stepped squarely in the middle of the canoe so that it wouldn't topple.

Mary's dad showed her how to use the paddle as a rudder at the end of each stroke to keep the canoe from going in a circle.

Then Mary tried it.

"You must have strong muscles," Dad said. "You are really doing well."

Mary was proud. She had learned to paddle a canoe without any trouble.

_____   _____   _____

_____   _____   _____

_____   _____   _____

_____   _____   _____

Write the words on the lines, dividing them into syllables.

candle   temple   drizzle   beetle   jungle   thimble   stable   apple   cradle

_____   _____   _____

_____   _____   _____

_____   _____   _____

Directions: In each grouping in the first section, make words by matching a syllable from the first column to a syllable in the second column. Write the words on the lines below. In the second section, use a word from the first section to complete each sentence.

Make words.

1. bub	fle	5. tur	dle	9. cir	tle
2. rat	dle	6. pud	ble	10. whis	cle
3. rid	ble	7. pur	tle	11. han	ple
4. ruf	tle	8. thim	ple	12. sim	dle

_____   _____   _____

_____   _____   _____

_____   _____   _____

_____   _____   _____

Complete each sentence, using a word from the section above.

1. The baby likes to play with his blue _____.

2. Blow the _____ when it is time to start the race.

3. Greta knows the answer to the _____.

4. The _____ walked slowly across the road.

5. Charles says that the arithmetic test is _____.

6. I cannot lift the pan because the _____ is too hot.

7. The children had fun splashing in the _____ after the rain.

8. One _____ John blew went over the roof and disappeared.

Directions: Read each rule, and draw lines through the words to divide them into syllables.

1. A one-syllable word is never divided.

   boat   good   knelt   smell

2. Divide a compound word between the words that make the compound word.

   pancake   sunset   airplane   baseball

3. When a word has a suffix, divide the word between the root word and the suffix.

   melted   softness   sewing   homeless

4. When a word has a prefix, divide the word between the prefix and the root word.

   expect   disturb   mislead   unsold

5. When two or more consonants come between two vowels in a word, the word is usually divided between the first two consonants.

   hungry   better   suffer   picture

6. When a single consonant comes between two vowels in a word, the word is usually divided after the consonant if the first vowel is short.

   clever   lemon   robin   travel

7. When a single consonant comes between two vowels in a word, the word is usually divided before the consonant if the first vowel is long.

   music   polar   paper   locate

8. When a vowel is sounded alone in a word, it forms a syllable in itself.

   disobey   alive   monument   uniform

9. When two vowels come together in a word and are sounded separately, divide the word between the two vowels.

   radio   diet   cruel   idea

10. When a word ends in **le** preceded by a consonant, divide the word before that consonant.

   turtle   cable   thistle   bicycle

Directions: On the first line after each word, write the numeral of the rule that is used to divide the word into syllables. On the second line, write the word, dividing it into syllables.

silk ___ _____   goodness ___ _____

painting ___ _____   hungry ___ _____

quiet ___ _____   alarm ___ _____

below ___ _____   cradle ___ _____

replant ___ _____   myself ___ _____

label ___ _____   rattle ___ _____

dune ___ _____   picture ___ _____

boulder ___ _____   driveway ___ _____

them ___ _____   locate ___ _____

ribbon ___ _____   minute ___ _____

magic ___ _____   thankful ___ _____

grapefruit ___ _____   knife ___ _____

ivy ___ _____   explain ___ _____

diet ___ _____   marble ___ _____

waited ___ _____   trial ___ _____

riot ___ _____   simple ___ _____

scribble ___ _____   mislead ___ _____

Directions: Complete each sentence by using the three-syllable word from the group of words at the right. Divide each word into syllables as you write it.

1. We _____ to make jelly last night.

   | intended |
   | started |
   | wanted |

2. Barbara was _____ when she saw her gift.

   | surprised |
   | happy |
   | excited |

3. The person who fixed our desks was a _____.

   | carpenter |
   | plumber |
   | electrician |

4. The dancer came in to _____ the guests.

   | invite |
   | surprise |
   | entertain |

5. The circus will _____ arrive in town today.

   | surely |
   | probably |
   | definitely |

6. The police _____ came and rescued the children.

   | officer |
   | sergeant |
   | patrol |

7. My baby brother was hiding _____ the porch.

   | upon |
   | underneath |
   | above |

8. Joe would sell more tickets if he would _____.

   | advertise |
   | travel |
   | work |

9. The _____ was unharmed by the fire.

   | furniture |
   | material |
   | goods |

10. I did not _____ my homework last night.

   | complete |
   | study |
   | understand |

11. Uncle Pete was on a _____ during the war.

   | battleship |
   | patrol |
   | airplane |

12. An orchestra is led by a _____.

   | violinist |
   | conductor |
   | drummer |

Directions: Write the words in the first section, dividing them into syllables. In the second section, draw lines through the underlined words to divide them into syllables.

Write the words, using hyphens to divide them into syllables.

armchair _____ open _____

forget _____ lonely _____

notice _____ refill _____

little _____ unfold _____

tiger _____ cowgirl _____

disagree _____ barrel _____

softly _____ repay _____

dislike _____ bluebird _____

Draw lines to divide the underlined words into syllables.

1. The tiger walked softly around his cage.
2. Boys and girls like to be helpful at home.
3. We sometimes help our dad clean the basement.
4. Yesterday we went shopping downtown.
5. The circus performer fell thirty-five feet to the sawdust below.
6. Sometimes Jeff is thoughtless and says unkind things.
7. The lonely old man sat in his armchair.
8. Helping people who need our help makes us happy.
9. Think of your actions, and see what kind of person you are trying to be.
10. Are you being faithful to your promises?

Directions: Write the words, using hyphens to divide them into syllables.

stainless	_____	fumble	_____
greatest	_____	peaceful	_____
strangely	_____	talking	_____
airport	_____	beehive	_____
create	_____	unwrap	_____
inside	_____	prepare	_____
Sunday	_____	haystack	_____
unkind	_____	forget	_____
sweetly	_____	icicle	_____
youngest	_____	neatness	_____
exactly	_____	heater	_____
bedroom	_____	lesson	_____
attention	_____	Diane	_____
contract	_____	jungle	_____
softer	_____	reply	_____
brighten	_____	barrel	_____
introduce	_____	broadcast	_____

Directions: Read about contractions. Then see if you can tell what each contraction stands for and which letter or letters are omitted.

REMEMBER:

A CONTRACTION is a short way of writing two words. It is formed by writing the two words together and leaving out one or more letters.

We always write an apostrophe (') to show where something is left out.

Example: I'm going to study.

I'm is the contraction for **I am**.

What letter was left out?

What is put in its place?

Sometimes two or more letters are left out.

Example: **we will** is written **we'll**

Write the two words the contraction stands for, and then write the letter or letters omitted.

Contractions	Meaning	Letters Left Out
isn't	_____	_____
there's	_____	_____
haven't	_____	_____
wouldn't	_____	_____
you've	_____	_____
let's	_____	_____
couldn't	_____	_____
don't	_____	_____
they've	_____	_____
he's	_____	_____

Directions: In the first section, write the contraction for each word group on the lines. In the second section, complete each sentence by using a contraction from the list at the right.

Read each word group in column 1. Find a contraction in column 2 for each word group and write it on the line.

1		2	1		2
I am	_____	I'll	were not	_____	can't
is not	_____	I'm	would not	_____	it's
I will	_____	isn't	it is	_____	wouldn't
we are	_____	I've	did not	_____	weren't
I have	_____	we're	can not	_____	didn't

1		2	1		2
you will	_____	let's	that is	_____	shouldn't
you are	_____	wasn't	they will	_____	aren't
let us	_____	we'll	do not	_____	that's
could not	_____	you'll	are not	_____	they'll
was not	_____	you're	he will	_____	don't
we will	_____	couldn't	should not	_____	he'll

Complete each sentence, using a contraction from the list at the right.

1. They _____ go through the forest.   I'm

2. Kenny _____ afraid when he heard the shrill whistle.   They'll

3. _____ afraid the canoe will not go under the bridge.   it's

4. _____ take their skates along on the trip.   wasn't

5. I think _____ going to be a fine day for a hike.   couldn't

Directions: Read the story, and draw a ring around each contraction. On the lines at the bottom of the page, write the two words that mean the same as each contraction you found.

Time for Safety

Peter and his little brother, Tom, hurried down the street on their way to school.

"I hope we're not late today," said Tom.

"We aren't late," said Peter. "And if we are, they'll wait for us."

"Do you think it'll rain?" asked Tom.

"We've been hoping for two weeks that it wouldn't rain," said Tom. "Just look at the sky. It couldn't rain if it wanted to. There's not a cloud in the sky."

The stop light was red as they came to the corner. Tom stepped off the curb.

"You'd better get back on the curb," said Peter. "You're not supposed to start crossing the street until the light turns green."

"Where's the policeman?" asked Tom. "He's not here. We won't get caught."

"It doesn't matter whether someone is watching you or not. Obey the safety rules all the time, and you won't get hurt. You don't want to get run over or hit by a car do you?" asked his big brother. "Can't you see yourself lying in a hospital while the rest of us are out having fun? Let's wait for the light."

The light changed. The boys looked both ways and then walked across the street. They could see the school yard, now, and the bus loaded with children. Across the front of the bus hung a big banner. It read Chartered Bus—Annual School Picnic.

1. _____   7. _____   13. _____

2. _____   8. _____   14. _____

3. _____   9. _____   15. _____

4. _____   10. _____   16. _____

5. _____   11. _____   17. _____

6. _____   12. _____   18. _____

Directions: Write the two words that mean the same as each contraction.

I'm	_____	aren't	_____
can't	_____	shouldn't	_____
couldn't	_____	didn't	_____
he's	_____	we'll	_____
doesn't	_____	let's	_____
here's	_____	you'll	_____
I've	_____	won't	_____
you're	_____	they've	_____
she's	_____	they're	_____
we've	_____	we're	_____
hadn't	_____	wouldn't	_____
weren't	_____	it's	_____
I'll	_____	she'll	_____
aren't	_____	wasn't	_____
they'll	_____	he'll	_____
there's	_____	isn't	_____
haven't	_____	don't	_____

Directions: From the list of words, find a synonym for the underlined word. Then write each sentence, using a synonym in place of the underlined word.

REMEMBER: SYNONYMS are words that have the same or almost the same meaning.

big — large   small — little   happy — jolly

---

guarded   story   woods   still   close   injure   house

1. The men searched for the lost boy in the <u>forest</u>. _____

_____

2. Please remember to <u>shut</u> the door quietly. _____

_____

3. Mom told the <u>tale</u> of "The Three Bears." _____

_____

4. They moved into their new <u>home</u>. _____

_____

5. The dog might <u>hurt</u> Baby Susan. _____

_____

6. Everyone was <u>quiet</u> as they listened for footsteps. _____

_____

7. The police officer <u>protected</u> the building. _____

_____

Directions: In the first section, use a word from the list at the top to answer each riddle. In the second section, match each pair of synonyms by placing the number of the word in the first column beside its synonym in the second column.

Answer the riddles.

woods   big   funny   hear   boat   close   beautiful

1. I have four letters. I mean the same as <u>listen</u>.   I am _____.

2. I tell about clowns. I mean the same as <u>comical</u>.   I am _____.

3. I have four letters. I mean the same as <u>ship</u>.   I am _____.

4. I have five letters. I mean the same as <u>near</u>.   I am _____.

5. I have three letters. I mean the same as <u>large</u>.   I am _____.

6. I have five letters. I mean the same as <u>forest</u>.   I am _____.

7. I have nine letters. I mean the same as <u>pretty</u>.   I am _____.

Match each pair of synonyms by placing the number of the word in column 1 beside its synonym in column 2.

1	2	1	2	1	2
1. fix	___ hurt	1. huge	___ spoke	1. say	___ drop
2. injure	___ gift	2. pretty	___ large	2. fall	___ little
3. present	___ repair	3. told	___ quiet	3. glisten	___ even
4. raise	___ remain	4. silent	___ glad	4. level	___ tell
5. stay	___ lift	5. happy	___ beautiful	5. small	___ sparkle

1	2	1	2	1	2
1. fearful	___ crawl	1. swift	___ attractive	1. postman	___ trip
2. reap	___ sad	2. handsome	___ dreary	2. strike	___ piece
3. creep	___ afraid	3. gloomy	___ marvelous	3. journey	___ mailman
4. big	___ gather	4. wonderful	___ informed	4. store	___ hit
5. unhappy	___ large	5. reported	___ speedy	5. part	___ shop

Directions: At the top, match the antonyms by placing the number for each word in Column 1 beside its antonym in Column 2. At the bottom, write a complete sentence to answer each question, using an antonym in place of the underlined word.

> **REMEMBER:** ANTONYMS are words that are opposite or almost opposite in meaning.

Match each pair of antonyms by placing the number of the word in Column 1 beside its antonym in Column 2.

1	2	1	2	1	2
1. strong	___ dry	1. light	___ tight	1. large	___ fearful
2. hot	___ dark	2. loose	___ warm	2. sharp	___ spend
3. many	___ cold	3. cool	___ dull	3. sick	___ dull
4. light	___ few	4. fat	___ heavy	4. fearless	___ healthy
5. wet	___ weak	5. bright	___ thin	5. save	___ small

1	2	1	2	1	2
1. asleep	___ fast	1. swiftly	___ quiet	1. hard	___ under
2. slow	___ awake	2. noisy	___ difficult	2. young	___ soft
3. friend	___ sad	3. easy	___ go	3. win	___ descend
4. full	___ enemy	4. build	___ slowly	4. over	___ old
5. happy	___ empty	5. come	___ destroy	5. climb	___ lose

Answer each question by using an antonym in place of the underlined word.

1. Is the new girl in your class <u>happy</u>? _____

_____

2. Was our class <u>noisy</u> during the fire drill? _____

_____

3. Was the test <u>hard</u>? _____

_____

Directions: Write an **S** on the line between each pair of words if they are synonyms; write an **A** if they are antonyms.

short	_____	long	foolish	_____	wise
sick	_____	healthy	woods	_____	forest
reap	_____	gather	friend	_____	enemy
high	_____	low	terrible	_____	awful
big	_____	large	hate	_____	love
quick	_____	swift	anybody	_____	nobody
looked	_____	hunted	idea	_____	plan
above	_____	below	hot	_____	cold
shut	_____	close	rush	_____	hurry
join	_____	separate	over	_____	under
quiet	_____	still	tall	_____	short
inside	_____	outside	display	_____	show
narrow	_____	wide	lost	_____	found
simple	_____	easy	joy	_____	sorrow
fast	_____	slow	powerful	_____	mighty
smoky	_____	clear	protect	_____	guard
well	_____	healthy	cool	_____	warm

Directions: Draw a ring around the word that correctly completes each sentence. Then write the word on the line at the right.

REMEMBER: HOMONYMS are words that sound alike but have different meanings and a different spelling.

---

1. We asked the (maid, made) to wash the windows. _____

2. The wind (blew, blue) the clouds across the sky. _____

3. Benita (cent, sent) her new puzzle to a little sick girl. _____

4. Carol (rode, road) in her brother's new car. _____

5. We are learning how to (right, write) letters. _____

6. Gus was very (weak, week) after being sick. _____

7. The stagecoach changed horses at the (in, inn). _____

8. Dale (through, threw) the ball and broke the window. _____

9. We (ate, eight) our supper when Grandma came home. _____

10. The doctor will (be, bee) here any minute. _____

11. He went to the store to (by, buy) a model plane. _____

12. Our baseball team (beat, beet) all the other teams. _____

13. Ross gave the bus driver his (fare, fair). _____

14. The film on rockets lasted one (our, hour). _____

15. Mary Ellen (red, read) about the two little rabbits. _____

Directions: Complete each sentence in the first section by choosing the correct word. In the second section, match each pair of homonyms.

Complete the sentences.

1. There was _____ on the grass this morning.   due   dew

2. The wind _____ the tree down.   blue   blew

3. I helped Mom _____ the apples.   peal   peel

4. Philip has a new _____ of shoes.   pair   pare

5. The baby picked a _____ in the garden.   flower   flour

6. The _____ of flowers was everywhere.   sent   scent

7. The man left only one _____ in the boat.   or   oar

8. Joseph tried to _____ through the hole.   peek   peak

9. Mary paid one _____ for the piece of candy.   cent   scent

Match each pair of homonyms by placing the number of the word in Column 1 beside its homonym in Column 2.

1	2	1	2	1	2
1. break	___ knot	1. ate	___ wrap	1. steak	___ bear
2. not	___ wait	2. ring	___ wring	2. bare	___ road
3. weight	___ brake	3. rap	___ eight	3. rode	___ stake

1	2	1	2	1	2
1. right	___ dye	1. I	___ sale	1. nose	___ son
2. see	___ sea	2. led	___ eye	2. pain	___ knows
3. die	___ write	3. sail	___ lead	3. sun	___ pane

Directions: In each box use the homonyms to complete the sentences.

1. The doctor traveled over the country _____. She _____

    over hills and through valleys to help the people.

    road   rode

2. Mom asked Kip to go to the store for _____. He asked if he might

    wait until later and _____ Dad when he came home from work.

    meet   meat

3. Linda was learning to sew. She did not _____ to mind at all the care

    and trouble it took to make a good strong _____.

    seem   seam

4. While we were busy carrying in _____ for the fireplace, Uncle Leo

    said he _____ prepare the steaks and the potatoes.

    wood   would

5. That play was the best I have ever _____. The last _____

    was the best part.

    scene   seen

6. Everyone was heading down the road to the county _____. The bus

    _____ was only twenty cents, but everyone was walking.

    fare   fair

LESSON 59: TEST: CONTRACTIONS, SYNONYMS, ANTONYMS, AND HOMONYMS

Directions: Follow the directions for each section.

Write the contractions.

I will _____   we are _____   you are _____

you would _____   did not _____   you will _____

he is _____   are not _____   I am _____

Write a synonym for each word.

shut _____   injure _____   repair _____

swift _____   gift _____   huge _____

small _____   lift _____   tale _____

Write an antonym for each word.

hot _____   heavy _____   many _____

come _____   slow _____   strong _____

soft _____   wet _____   sharp _____

Write a homonym for each word.

dear _____   our _____   cell _____

bee _____   buy _____   break _____

here _____   fair _____   peace _____

LESSON 59: REVIEWING CONTRACTIONS, SYNONYMS, ANTONYMS, AND HOMONYMS

Directions: Work the crossword puzzle.

ACROSS

1. a synonym for <u>noisiest</u>

6. an antonym for <u>cold</u>

8. a synonym for <u>everyone</u> or <u>everything</u>

9. a synonym for <u>look</u>

10. a synonym for <u>still</u>

12. tools for chopping wood

14. the beginning of a plant

15. a synonym for <u>vote</u>

16. a homonym for <u>pair</u>

18. spun wool or cotton

20. a homonym for <u>die</u>

22. the contraction for <u>I have</u>

23. a synonym for <u>bed</u>

24. a synonym for <u>hurry</u>

25. an antonym for <u>joys</u>

DOWN

1. a synonym for <u>depart</u>

2. an antonym for <u>beautiful</u>

3. the opposite of <u>west</u>

4. a homonym for <u>their</u>

5. an antonym for appear

7. a synonym for <u>lateness</u>

11. a synomym for <u>each</u>

13. a homonym for <u>sea</u>

14. a synonym for <u>pigpen</u>

17. a synonym for <u>destroys</u>

19. short for <u>automobiles</u>

20. a homonym for <u>dear</u>

21. a sound reflected back

159

DEFINITIONS AND RULES

The **vowels** are **a, i, u, o, e**, and sometimes **y** and **w**.

The **consonants** are the remaining letters and usually **y** and **w**.

A **consonant blend** consists of two or more consonants sounded together in such a way that each is heard—**black**, **train**, **cry**, **swim**, **spring**.

A **consonant digraph** consists of two consonants that together represent one sound—**when**, **thin**, **this**, **church**, **sheep**, **pack**, **know**, **write**.

An **irregular double vowel** is a double vowel that does not follow Long-Vowel Rule I—**school**, **book**, **bread**, **auto**, **yawn**, **eight**.

A **diphthong** consists of two vowels blended together to form a compound speech sound—**cloud**, **boy**, **oil**, **cow**, **new**.

Short-Vowel Rule: If a word or syllable has only one vowel and it comes at the beginning or between two consonants, the vowel usually stands for a short sound—**am**, **is**, **bag**, **fox**.

Long-Vowel Rule I: If a one-part word or syllable has two vowels, the first vowel usually stands for a long sound and the second is silent—**rain**, **kite**, **cane**, **jeep**.

Long-Vowel Rule II: If a word or syllable has one vowel and it comes at the end of the word or syllable, the vowel usually stands for a long sound—**we**, **go**, **cupid**, **pony**.

Y As a Vowel Rule:
1) If **Y** is the only vowel at the end of a one-syllable word, **Y** stands for the sound of long **I**—**fly**, **try**, **by**.
2) If **Y** is the only vowel at the end of a word of more than one syllable, **Y** usually stands for a sound almost like long **E**—**silly**, **funny**, **baby**.

Soft C and G Rule: When **c** or **g** is followed by **e**, **i**, or **y**, it is usually soft—**ice**, **city**, **change**, **gym**.